'Silas!' Rachael tore her mouth from his, outrage leaping from her eyes which his slow, knowing smile did nothing to ease, nor the fact that he had failed to increase the distance between them.

'Geoffrey must have ice in his veins. Either that or more patience than most males would wish to possess.'

'Why, you. . .!' A strangled sound broke from her throat and Silas caught her wrists, muffling an oath when her toe caught his ankle.

'You're certainly an old-fashioned girl, considering you pack quite a punch for an amateur.' He laughed at her speechless fury, forcing her hands behind her back so that she couldn't attempt to do what her eyes were threatening. 'I promise, saving yourself for me is definitely one of your better decisions.'

THE
PARIS TYPE

BY

CHRISTINE GREIG

MILLS & BOON LIMITED
ETON HOUSE   18–24 PARADISE ROAD
RICHMOND   SURREY   TW9 1SR

First published in Great Britain 1991
by Mills & Boon Limited

© Christine Greig 1991

Australian copyright 1991
Philippine copyright 1991
This edition 1991

ISBN 0 263 77243 8

Set in 10 on 11 pt Linotron Times
01-9109-58612
Typeset in Great Britain by Centracet, Cambridge
Made and printed in Great Britain

CHAPTER ONE

GRETA IBBOTSON peered over her spectacles as the head of Tredegar and Pitt returned from a business trip with the air of an undoubted conqueror. Silas Tredegar had been back in New York for only a matter of hours. He had caught an earlier flight than had been expected and consequently the usual busy hubbub of activity in the building had increased to something approaching panic.

Those in the inner sanctum exhibited an enviable calm in the face of what others considered a disaster. Silas Tredegar's office staff were used to their leader's erratic behaviour. They had stayed the pace when weaker mortals had resigned in various forms of hysteria. True, Rachael James, Silas's personal assistant, had come in on her day off, but she hadn't waited through her lunch break and in Tredegar and Pitt that smacked of heady self-confidence.

Rachael, Greta mused, was getting decidedly prickly where Silas was concerned. The grapevine was positively humming after the last clash over holidays. She paused in her thoughts, greeting her boss with a warmth that owed something to affection as well as professional courtesy. He smiled in his usual manner, as if he was satisfied with the décor, rather than noticing the person behind the desk, and went on to his office.

Greta began to count slowly. 'One, two, three——'

The door, so recently closed, was flung back on its hinges and Greta blinked, more with the sudden rush of disturbed air than any feeling of surprise.

'Did you want something, Mr Tredegar?' she asked

soothingly, making the appropriate noises, even though she doubted that he heard a word she said. 'How was London?'

He stared at the empty desk opposite Greta's with a look of non-comprehension, holding in his hand a half-opened package containing, Greta guessed, perfume. She had received a similar package, not so expensive or, she guessed again, so long in the choosing. Whatever Silas felt about his personal assistant, he certainly preferred that piece of office furniture to be exquisitely perfumed.

'Didn't she like it?' he asked, rather touchingly perplexed for a class 'A' male chauvinist. 'Well. . .?' He plonked it down on her desk, thrusting his hands in his trouser pockets and turning to stare at the empty desk as if Rachael James would appear under his commanding glare. 'I don't understand her. Other women like flowers and perfume. I think she does it deliberately to irritate me.' He swung around on his heel, blue eyes certainly irritated, making an incongruous contrast with his perfectly groomed black hair.

He was, Greta had to admit, the most handsome man she had ever met. She was fifty and had seen some hunks in her time but Silas Tredegar was in a class of his own. Blessed with the face of a film star and the broad shoulders and narrow hips of a male model, he would raise a flutter in the most matronly female breast. It was a pleasure to study the way his suits worshipped his lean body and she would bet money that Rachael James wasn't as impervious as she pretended.

'Perhaps she's got an allergy,' she threw out, her inspiration deflated by the dry tone she used. 'She does seem to be developing a phobia about florists.'

Nothing penetrated that thick skin, Greta decided. Rachael didn't hide her displeasure at being sent on missions for personal gifts for Silas's numerous women friends and had more than once stated that if a man sent her red roses she'd pin him as a womaniser and ditch him immediately.

'She wears perfume,' he muttered, dark lashes narrowing. 'Where is she, anyway? I've got a stack of correspondence to deal with.' He moved to the window as if he would be able to spot her from the sixteenth floor and Greta smiled quietly to herself.

'Gordon's taken her to lunch.'

'Geoffrey,' he corrected shortly, his shoulders stiff, and he pried the blinds apart. The warmth of the sun was in stark contrast to the capricious weather May offered in England.

'You usually call him Gordon.' Greta's New York accent was a marked contrast to the cultured English tone of his. 'I didn't want to complicate things.'

'Comedian,' he growled under his breath, but she heard and her grin widened.

'Rachael's a good secretary,' she pointed out with a frankness born of long association. 'And a nice girl. It would be a mistake to play too close to home, Silas.'

There was a tension-crackling silence when the head of Tredegar and Pitt towered every inch of his six-foot-two frame over her and then put his hands on her desk and bent his head to look her straight in the eye.

'What makes you think I'd be playing?' he asked expressionlessly. Black brows drew together, eyes darkening to navy as they became thoughtful. 'Do you think she's serious about this clown Geoffrey?'

Greta felt relieved that the expected explosion had detonated harmlessly. 'I think he's hooked. Rachael doesn't talk much about her private life. Besides, married women don't necessarily give up their jobs, so why worry?'

Silas straightened, his grey suit miraculously losing its creases and taking on its former perfection. He didn't look as if he liked that idea one bit.

'We travel a lot.' He noted Greta's quirky little smile, his expression darkening.

'This had better be her lunch break!' He glowered at her, professional charm suddenly missing.

Greta winced as the connecting door to Silas's office hurtled back into the frame, sending vibrations throughout the entire office.

Rachael eased her foot out of her shoe, wishing she hadn't bought such a high heel. She was five feet six and didn't really need the extra height but Geoffrey's massive six and a half feet allowed her to indulge the desire to look leggy. 'Never again,' she moaned, rubbing her sole, wondering if there was something missing in the genes of prairie folk that made the adaptation to stilettos impossible. She smiled at the thought but her humour soon abated when she remembered the family problem that had recalled her to Iowa when she should have accompanied Silas to London.

Her brother's gambling addiction was draining their parents' resources and they had wanted her to talk to Michael and try to make him see sense. Rachael had quickly summed up the situation: her brother was spoilt and farming bored him; two underlying factors to the problem that she knew her parents wouldn't want to hear. Rolling corn and soybean fields stretching as far as the eye could see might sound like paradise to those brought up in the city. But would they swap the crowds and fast cars for isolation and a pick-up truck? It was a matter of taste. Her parents loved it. Rachael, though not over-enamoured with cities, shared her brother's wanderlust. Whether it had done her any good or not was a moot point.

She flexed her toes, glad to have the blood circulating once more. On the face of it, she supposed, she was successful. Her secretarial skills and flair for organis-ation had taken her to the top of her profession. She travelled widely, had her own apartment, car and an expense account that took care of most of her wardrobe. The only fly in the ointment was Silas Tredegar. She had parted on less than cordial terms with her employer because the first week of his business trip clashed with her holiday plans. He had put her through hellfire before he left and yet the fact that he was back made her heart lift with gladness. Seeing Geoffrey, after a week's absence, hadn't made her blood race with such a feeling of anticipation, and the knowledge had contributed to the flash temper that had made her return Silas's gift.

The truth of the matter was that she was still suffering from the lingering pangs of infatuation. During the first six months she had worked for Silas, Rachael had developed an almighty crush on him that made every working hour paradise. No wonder he had come to expect her devoted attention. Working late, accompanying him on his trips abroad, had been a blessing not a curse. She had been twenty-two then and fresh to the big city; now, three years later, she still felt her heart race every time he appeared unexpectedly and all the little defence mechanisms she had developed over the years ceased to work.

The sound of a door opening made her look up sharply. A dark shadow momentarily blocked off the sunlight streaming through the windows. A breathless seizure restricted Rachael's lungs and she struggled to adopt an expression of polite welcome, but gave up when it became clear that he had no intention of following suit.

'Planning to type with your toes, Miss James?' Silas sat on the edge of her desk, arms crossed, his mouth ominously straight. 'I know your hours have a certain flexibility, but it would be nice if you could be in the office some time during my working day. It's rather difficult having a personal secretary one never sees.'

She took in at a glance his silver-grey suit, crisp blue shirt and matching tie and wondered how he could look so cool when she felt hot and flustered.

'A slight exaggeration, Mr Tredegar.' She continued to massage her foot. 'This is supposed to be my day off. I came in because you decided to come back ahead of schedule.' 'Put that in your pipe and smoke it' was unsaid but wrapped around every word, and Rachael's dark eyes reinforced each syllable.

Meeting her gaze, Silas appeared to reconsider his approach. Absence had dulled her reflexes and the warning bells went off too late.

'Do I detect a degree of hostility in your voice?' He caught her wrist between his thumb and index finger and cast it aside, bending down and grasping her ankle, resting the heel against his thigh and continuing the massage. 'If so, perhaps you could air your grievance while I soothe the pain from your foot. I'm told I'm very good at this.' He smiled into her annoyed and slightly flushed features. She was rattled and he knew it; Silas's sudden change of tactics was predictable but still left her reeling.

'Rachael,' he enquired, his voice dropping several octaves, 'why did you return my present? Don't struggle. . .' a wicked determination underlaid the charm '. . .or I'll tickle you. We'll end up on the floor and your reputation will be in shreds.' His sharkish grin inflamed her.

' I feel ridiculous!' she hissed, trying to keep the skirt of her business suit straight. Her long chestnut-coloured hair shone in the bright slashes of light from the window. Wide brows, usually gracefully arched, knotted in fury, her eyes lightened to sherry by the sun's brilliance. 'You don't have to give me presents. I get paid well enough to buy my own perfume and I don't particularly like that brand. Does that satisfy you?'

She tried to disguise the defensive note in her voice but they were both aware of it. Rachael had returned the perfume on impulse. She had shopped for gifts for the girls in the office often enough to know that Silas merely signed a cheque and hadn't a clue what was inside the professionally wrapped packages. It wasn't until she was faced with the man that she had realised that her rejection would have more significance than polite acceptance. She resented being a name on his temporary secretary's list and she could kick herself for letting him know it.

'It was a peace offering.' He let her off the hook, pretending that she was still smarting from the uncomfortable week that had followed her refusal to go to London with him. 'I'm trying to say I'm sorry.' His fingers were delicately caressing her arch while he concentrated all his attention upon her face. 'Greta's pleased with her perfume. Tell me what you'd like, Rachael.'

'How would you like me to slap a sexual harassment suit on you?' She couldn't climb down to save her life. 'I'd like my foot back, Mr Tredegar.'

He smiled, white teeth gleaming, releasing her without preamble. 'Certainly.' He remained impervious to her prickly reception. 'Miss me?'

Rachael bent to retrieve her shoe, glad of the diversion. 'It's quiet when you're away,' she returned, pushing her foot back into place. 'Did you want to start work? I've dealt with most of the correspondence Mr Mackenzie didn't take care of but there were a few things. . .'

'I've looked through my tray,' he returned noncommittally, his blue eyes still studying her but with a faraway look in them. 'Have you seen to my apartment?'

'Yes. You've got enough food and alcohol to last you a month.' She wished he would go, so she could calm herself and return to the cool secretarial efficiency which she usually affected.

'Have dinner with me tonight.' He stood up, smiling down at her with the kind of innocence he certainly didn't remember. Probably practised in front of the mirror, she decided sourly.

'I call a halt at cooking, ironing and keeping your company when you're too tired to consult your little black book.' She tried unsuccessfully to keep the heat from her cheeks.

'I'll do the cooking,' he promised, watching the tell-tale wave of colour with a hateful smile in his eyes. 'Don't worry.' He turned away. 'It's business. I don't want that beefcake Geoffrey breaking down the door. Take the rest of the day off and turn up around seven,' he threw over his shoulder before disappearing into his office.

'It *is* my day off,' she flung after him, and then tried to compose herself as John Mackenzie hurried past her to consult his lord and master. Gathering her things, she left the office to salvage what was left of her day off.

Later, she wished she had been more composed. She hadn't the faintest idea how many people would be there for dinner or whom she should pay special attention to. Picking up the phone, she rang into the office, found that Silas was in conference and spoke to Greta instead.

'He's grilling Mackenzie, I can hear John's knees knocking from here. By the way. . .' there was a pause '. . . His Highness didn't appreciate his perfume being returned. If I didn't know him better, I'd say you'd upset him.'

'Silas? I doubt that. Do you know anything about a dinner party tonight at his apartment? He didn't give me many details. Did he mention anything to you about it?'

'No, I'll look in the diary. . .'

'No point, there's nothing in there about this. Never mind, could you ask him to call me when he has a minute?'

'Sure. But trying to stop a whirlwind isn't that easy. I'm surprised he let you have the day off.'

'It *is* my day off,' she reminded the older woman, putting the receiver back into its cradle, none the wiser.

Silas hadn't contacted her by six and she knew by then that he wasn't going to. She tried to pick something to wear that would be suitable for a small dinner party and not look odd at a larger gathering.

Geoffrey called while she was surveying her wardrobe. She held up a soft jersey dress for his approval. It was black with a full skirt and a lace-up back. If his response was anything to go by it was certainly a success.

'Wearing that tonight? It's terrific!' He grinned appreciatively.

'Tonight? Oh, Geoffrey. . .' She looked apologetic. 'Silas commanded my presence at a dinner party he's holding this evening. I forgot all about going to the theatre—I'm sorry.'

He ran his hand through his mop of golden hair. As a sports coach for Marshall High he swapped complimentary tickets with the drama teacher. She knew he did it for her benefit; he wasn't keen on the theatre.

'But Rachael, he can't just mess up your social life like that. God, he's only been back a minute and he's doing it again. Are you sure he isn't interested in you? It seems like he's always wanting you for something.'

'Silas doesn't even see me in that way,' she reassured him, ignoring the twinge of pain that recognised the truth of her statement. 'He's selfish; he probably thinks I sit by the phone waiting to be activated by his call.'

'You could have refused to go.'

'I'm sorry, I'm afraid I forgot about this evening.' Forgot everything under the teasing gaze of a pair of extremely sexy blue eyes, she admitted to herself crossly.

Geoffrey was clearly disgruntled. 'Being selfish seems to pay. I'm surprised he hasn't suggested you move in with him. It would be so much more convenient.'

'Not really. It would cramp his style.' She patted his arm. 'Don't pretend you wouldn't rather watch the game on TV. I'll have to get ready.' She smiled at his consternation. 'I feel obliged to go. After all, I refused to go to London with him and he was furious about that.'

'I suppose the money's good,' he relented grudgingly. 'And if we get married——'

'Geoffrey, not so fast.' She put her hand over his mouth, her brown eyes gentle. 'I. . . Let's discuss this tomorrow. Silas will blow a fuse if I'm late.'

'Wouldn't that be terrible?' he grunted, throwing up his hands in defeat. 'OK, I'm going. I'll ring you later. Make sure you leave with the others. I don't trust that guy.'

'I'm over twenty-one,' she reminded him a little sharply. 'I can look after myself, don't worry.'

'Yeah.' He rubbed his hand around the back of his neck. 'I'd still rather be with you than watch the game.' He bent and kissed her cheek. 'You can tell me about the evening later.'

'Silas's dinner parties can go on for a while,' she cautioned, trying hard not to resent his show of possessiveness. After all, she had been dating Geoffrey for over six months. It wasn't natural to expect him to like the idea of her spending the evening with another man.

'I'll ring at twelve.' He moved to the door. 'He can't expect you to stay longer than that.'

'Huh?' Rachael's scepticism was lost on the sports coach and she hurried to get dressed as the door closed behind him.

Rachael drove her Renault to the expensive and elegant part of Manhattan that provided Silas's base while he was in New York. It was situated on the outskirts of the rectangular piece of borough that contained the famed Times Square, Carnegie Hall and Madison Square Garden. More importantly for her employer, it also happened to be on the doorstep of the best theatres and most exclusive restaurants and nightclubs New York had to offer.

Silas was a city bird, she reflected; he liked the bright lights. When he was in London, he always stayed in a Knightsbridge hotel; she couldn't imagine him working on the land, sweating under a hot sun, dressed in dungarees. She laughed out loud at the thought. The only thing that puzzled her slightly was his address in Cornwall. From what she had gleaned about the wild and rocky west of England, it hardly fitted in with Silas's cosmopolitan image.

Parking the Renault in the underground car park, she took the short lift ride up to the ground floor, having to pass the security desk before gaining access to the interior of the building.

'Got you running after him already, has he?' She was greeted by the man on duty. She smiled ruefully, thinking that was exactly what Silas had done.

'Hi, there, Leo. Yes, when hasn't he? Has anyone else gone up to his suite yet?'

'No.' He shook his head, consulting his book. 'He only mentioned you. Nobody else.'

She frowned. 'That's odd. I'll ring down and give you the guest list in a few minutes. He's got a lot on his mind,' she apologised for him, accustomed to making excuses for his lapses. 'He must have forgotten.'

That's why they made a good team, she mused. She was meticulous in detail. Silas wasn't rude or ill mannered; he was just careless where minutiae was concerned. Having been working for him for three years, Rachael knew all his faults yet still found him an intriguing man. Everything he did appeared so effortless. His work, his harem of women, all passed in an uninterrupted flow of impressive success. On the work side, she knew he had an intuitive grasp of property development that had secured his position as the head of the company at an early age. His success with women she didn't ponder too deeply. She had the vague feeling that something was missing from his relationships, but then fun and only fun might be all he demanded from his lady friends.

Fuelled by her thoughts, her thumb made an angry stab at the doorbell and she moved back a step as the door opened almost immediately.

Ah, Rachael.' Silas greeted her with a smile that made her knees quake. Not that usual absent smile but fully attentive, his eyes fixed on her stunned expression. 'You're on time. How efficient. Come in.'

She walked into the apartment, a cold shiver feathering her spine as he removed her coat. Something in the way his fingers brushed the bare skin of her shoulder signalled alarm. She was quite prepared to believe it was her imagination but she could have sworn she felt his warm breath against her neck.

'Silas. . .?'

'What would you like to drink?' He moved from behind her, her coat over his arm, meeting her disturbed eyes with a suspicious blandness in his. 'The meal's Greek but the wine's Italian. I've opened a bottle, if you want a glass.'

'Wine will be fine. Silas. . .?'

'Won't be a minute.' He held up a hand, staving off her curiosity, and disappeared with her coat.

Frowning, she let her eyes drift over the familiar furnishings. The apartment had been designed on lines of boldness and clarity. Squashy black leather couches faced each other like two kings on a chessboard. Sketches of English holiday towns adorned the white walls, square rosewood occasional tables defied the decorative nature of the wood and posed the same sense of definition and purpose. Video and cassette libraries occupied stark shelf systems, the former containing among others the Ealing comedies and Laurel and Hardy, the latter a selection of classical music, rock 'n' roll and jazz tapes. Rachael found it hard to imagine kicking her shoes off and watching an old film in the apartment; it looked the sort of place that demanded good wine and intelligent conversation.

Her thoughts were disturbed when her employer returned, crooked a finger and led the way into the kitchen.

'Silas?' She determinedly followed him, perching herself on a stool beside the breakfast bar as he checked everything was as it should be. He flicked her a quick glance and turned his attention to the wine.

'Mmm? You keep on parroting my name. What's so important?'

'You didn't give Leo a guest list,' she pointed out with mock patience, not liking the evasive attitude he was taking. 'It won't create the right impression if your guests aren't expected.'

'What guests?' He looked baffled. 'I told him you were coming, didn't I?' His brows drew together as he came around to her side of the bench and deposited the wine at her elbow. He moved on to peer into the oven. 'Moussaka,' he informed her. 'You like that, I remember.'

Rachael twisted around to study him. 'No one else?' she queried, determined to get her facts straight. 'Just me?'

'Just you. We have things to discuss.'

She picked up her glass, her mind racing. What was he up to? She had expected some kind of showdown during the week of hostilities before his departure for London. When it hadn't come, she had rather flatteringly assumed he didn't want to risk losing her.

'What's wrong with the office?' she queried, her voice forced into calmness. 'I broke a date tonight to come here. I suppose it didn't occur to you that I might be otherwise occupied.'

'Yes.' He held up a finger. 'Actually, that's one of the reasons you're here.' He picked up his wine glass and took a mouthful. Dressed in a black wool suit, maroon tie and pocket handkerchief, he was well groomed as usual but there was something about his manner that suggested he was uncomfortable. 'Shall we go into the lounge? This isn't the sort of conversation best suited to kitchens.'

Rachael acquiesced, curiosity overwhelming her initial wariness. Taking the armchair he indicated, she looked expectantly at him, while he chose to remain standing. His free hand tugged his tie loose. If he was going to fire her, he was making a bad job of it, she mused, but found it hard to take the possibility seriously. They were friends. If it came to dismissal it would be in the heat of a row, not a pre-dinner chat.

'I trust you.' He avoided her eyes, seeming fascinated by the contents of his glass. 'I'm fond of you.' A dry laugh escaped him. 'God, I knew I'd make a mess of this.' He raked his fingers through his fringe and she watched, fascinated, as the dark, silky strands fell silently back into place. Strangely enough, the moment when Silas crossed the boundary between their professional relationship into something more personal she felt a peculiar sense of detachment.

'I'd better start at the beginning.' The beginning didn't seem any easier. He took another mouthful of wine to fortify himself before placing his glass on one of the occasional tables and reaching for his wallet. 'What I'm about to tell you is strictly confidential; I must have your word that it won't go beyond these four walls. Not so much for myself, but it would hurt someone I care for.' He came towards her, taking a photograph out of his wallet, and sat on the side of her chair, handing it to her, as her quiet 'Of course' sealed her promise.

Whatever she had expected, it wasn't the image of a small boy, who apart from his youthful features was a replica of Silas Tredegar.

'His name is Tris, short for Tristan.' He took a folded piece of paper out of his wallet and gave it to her. 'Look at the birth certificate.'

She obeyed in frozen silence, numbly taking in the information it revealed. Silas was named as the father and an unknown woman, Mary Deal, as the child's mother.

'Why are you showing me this?' she asked, returning the birth certificate, her dark eyes blank when he refused to accept it and pointed at the date of birth.

'We were in Japan in March; in April we spent the month covering the Denver project and New York after that. The child isn't mine, whether it was a short pregnancy or longer than usual—I wasn't in Britain at the appropriate time. I can prove that easily enough if I wanted to; however, that isn't the problem in question.' He took the photograph and certificate from her unresisting fingers, replacing them in his wallet. 'The child's mother is dead and therefore I have suddenly become a parent, a circumstance I didn't envisage when my cousin asked me to act as a front for him in the matter.'

Silas sighed, maintaining his position on the arm of

her chair, a slight smile disturbing the repose of his lips as he noted her relieved expression. 'Whatever my sins, Rachael, I don't play outside my own field. Young, inexperienced women I leave to young, inexperienced men.' A long finger stroked down her nose as if she were a favourite tabby cat he chose to indulge. 'There are two ways out of this,' he continued, as she struggled with the thought that he considered her in the category of the young and inexperienced. 'I have no desire to expose my family's skeletons to public viewing, so I'm left with the choice of rearing the child on my own or leaving him to the indifference of hired help.'

Rachael frowned. 'Your cousin's married, I suppose?'

Nodding, he declined to elaborate; getting up, he took the centre of the floor after repossessing his wine glass. 'I'm thirty-four—it's time I settled down.' He didn't look totally convinced about that. 'My own childhood was a lonely one. I think this little chap. . .' he patted his breast pocket '. . .deserves all the help he can get.'

Rachael felt a stirring of warmth at Silas's concern. It showed a depth of feeling she had always considered regrettably lacking. She cast her mind over his female acquaintances, trying to picture any of them in the role of wife and mother, and failed. The question died on her lips as she became trapped by the power of his gaze.

'You're a woman of strong loyalties, Rachael. I dare say you have a romantic view of marriage. I haven't,' he admitted honestly. 'The qualities I would seek for a brief fling in Paris are hardly those best suited to motherhood or the stability of a family. If you'd agree to be my wife, you have my solemn promise I'd honour the relationship. And, of course, I'd give you all the time you needed to get used to living with me.' He paused, waiting for a response, gleaning nothing from her expression, which was rather comically blank. 'Shall I make some hot, sweet tea? You look in a state of shock.'

She was! During the six months of blind adoration, she had had dreams about the moment Silas would suddenly reveal his feelings for her and ask her to be his wife. This, although far more realistic, trampled over such tender fantasies. She had thought Silas's whirlwind romances were shallow but she had never labelled him cold-blooded. But what else could you call a man who adopted a child to avoid family scandal, decided it was time to settle down, and looked no further than his office for a suitable candidate? She didn't need tea, she needed oxygen!

She took a deep breath, and her cheeks coloured as she noted that his attention was momentarily diverted to the rise and fall of her breasts. Blue eyes raised to hers, an element of masculine curiosity in their depths that made her want to cover herself up.

'You can't possibly think I could accept.' She spoke with heat. 'It would be a disaster. We don't love each other.'

His brief laugh was cynical. 'But you want me, don't you, Rachael? I'm not an unperceptive man; I've known that from the first day we met. If you'll excuse the cliché, you're the type of woman one would feel obliged to take home to Mother, so I didn't exploit the situation. That's not to say I wasn't interested,' he dared to tease her. 'I think half the reason I sent so many flowers was to gauge whether you still felt the same way. Your eyes are very expressive. Once or twice I've been tempted to send you roses just to see the fireworks.'

'Silas! Shut up!'

'Something like that, I should imagine.'

'How dare you?'

'Magnificent,' he applauded, a mixture of charm and good humour taking away any suggestion of mockery.

Silas was back on home ground, she acknowledged, not realising she was staring. No longer awkward, he was playing her to shore like a gasping fish. A surge of anger rushed through her veins, making her eyes glitter like dark rivers in a storm.

'You're an attractive man.' She didn't attempt to deny his words. 'At one time I thought you were more than that but three years in your company taught me some valuable lessons.' She stood up, smoothing the skirt of her dress with a shaking hand. He followed the gesture, still calm in the face of the tumult of her anger, but all the humour had disappeared, his features toughening to show the steel lurking beneath the charm.

And what, may I ask, did you learn?' he queried, his voice clipped and concise. 'That refusing my gifts was a more effective way of being noticed than accepting them? That you'd rather be regarded as an equal or friend that one of my brief flirtations?' He put his glass down, blocking her path as she tried to walk past him to the door. 'If I thought you loved Geoffrey I wouldn't be making this offer.' He caught her arm, his fingers holding her easily. 'I could have courted you for a few months and you'd have forgotten he even existed.'

'Will you get my coat, please?' Her teeth were clenched but she bared enough of them to give him adequate warning.

Something ignited in Silas's eyes, a hard cutting flame. 'No.' His mouth barely formed the word. 'I haven't finished.'

'Well, I have! You don't own me, Mr Tredegar, you just employ me.'

She tried to pull her arm free only to jar it painfully. Her cry of pain was met by an instinctive movement of Silas's hand to her shoulder, in a soothing but firm massage.

'I'm sorry,' he murmured into the heated silence, frowning at the suspicious gleam of tears in her eyes.

She looked down, escaping his penetrating gaze, not wanting to let him see how much his cavalier treatment of her private life had disturbed her. What was even more painful was the suspicion that everything he had said was true. She didn't love Geoffrey, she wanted Silas, and yet accepting his cynical proposal was beyond her. It violated everything she held sacred.

'Silas, children don't just go away. They're there for life. It would be cruel to offer. . . Tris a false security, don't you see that? You can't just treat the boy as another business deal. You. . .you might find someone you really care about.' She raised damp lashes to impress the seriousness of what he was proposing upon him. 'You can't just hire and fire mothers for him; it wouldn't work.'

'I trust you,' he repeated his earlier statement, his lean fingers continuing to ease over her shoulder. 'You're one of the few women I actually know beyond a good figure and a beautiful face. I think we'd be good for each other. It's a fair exchange. You want to leave that safe corner of yours and taste the edge of excitement. I want stability for a child and myself. I can give you everything you need.' His voice slid easily into a hypnotic purr. His hand left her shoulder, stroking her hair back behind her ear, and before she could anticipate his next move his head bent and he caught her lobe between his teeth, nipping it audaciously.

Rachael's reaction was instinctive. She slapped him hard across the face then moved back, fearing retaliation, and jumping with surprise when he laughed, rubbing his jaw with reluctant admiration in his eyes.

'Stability doesn't seem quite so boring all of a sudden,' he drawled, taking something else out of his breast pocket. He handed her a cheque and she looked at it, white with fury when she saw that it was drawn on his account for the amount of thirty thousand dollars.

'All it needs is my signature,' he informed her. 'And, before you give vent to all that righteous fury, it's not to buy you with. At least not directly,' he amended, closing the gap between them a trifle warily. He touched her arm, indicating that she should sit down. She refused, resentment written plainly on her face.

'Rachael.' His voice softened and there was an element of sympathy in his regard. 'When you refused to come to London with me I did some checking up of my own. At first I thought Geoffrey was the reason you were being so stubborn and then, of course, I discovered you'd gone home to Iowa.' He tapped the cheque with his index finger. 'Michael has got himself into more trouble than you know; that should clear his debts, all but about five thousand. The rest he'll owe to me and he'll work for it out of his salary.'

Rachael was stunned. Thirty-five thousand dollars! How could anyone be stupid enough to fritter away that much money? Her mind flew from one possibility to another. Could she get a loan? Would her parents have to remortgage the farm? And then there was no guarantee that Michael wouldn't do the same thing again. He needed a firm hand, someone to look up to and admire. Someone whom he could emulate.

'His salary? He doesn't really get a salary. Only an allowance—the farm. . .'

'No, I'm going to employ him here, where I can keep an eye on him and introduce him to some milder vices.' He hooked a finger under her chin, scanning her bruised eyes and vulnerable mouth with an unmasked determination that shocked her. 'We'll be married before we leave for Cornwall at the end of the month. Don't look so damn sacrificial; I'm doing you a favour.'

'No, you're not, Mr Tredegar. I haven't agreed to anything yet.' She jerked her chin from his grasp, chestnut hair cascading in a rush of fire over her shoulders. 'It's a large amount of money, but if I have to sell everything I own it will be worth it to stay out of your clutches.' Rebellion shone in her eyes, demanding his attention. She was determined that for once he would really see her, not that polite, patient caricature that clocked in from nine to five. 'I have no intention of slotting into your personal life like some pre-programmed robot. I'm a person! I have feelings! I find all this downright insulting.'

Silas allowed her to vent her indignation without interrupting but remained implacable. 'Unjust, certainly,' he agreed. 'Neither of us is responsible for the mess we're in. I can't cut free of my family ties; I doubt if you can yours. But. . .' he made a speaking gesture with his hands '. . .by all means explore every avenue open to you. I warn you now, though,' his voice was soft but made her eyes widen with apprehension, 'I won't help you escape.'

Rachael didn't reply. Their conversation had taken on an air of unreality. Whatever happened now, Silas had irretrievably changed the nature of their relationship. How could she continue working for him when his casual disposal of her personal life showed how lightly he regarded her as a person? Even if she could swallow that, it was doubtful that he would want a spectator when he went in search of another candidate for the role of wife and mother.

Later, when she was alone, she stared unseeingly at the ceiling, her mind a jumble of thoughts. Silas was an enigma to her, she realised. That surprised Rachael, because she had rather arrogantly presumed that she knew the man. Charming, successful, but incapable of deep commitment would have been her verdict if given that morning. Now she could only wonder at the depth of loyalty that bound him to the Tredegar family. It was as deep as her own. They were both victims of family excess but that did nothing to soothe her hurt feelings. He had been aware of the nagging infatuation that made her intensely vulnerable to him and had convinced himself that her fulfilment lay in being given his name and sharing his bed. A tide of hot embarrassment made her cringe. He had cruelly exposed her, without a thought for how that would make her feel. She had her own life! How dared he intrude like that?

Guiltily, her mind turned to Geoffrey. During Silas's proposal and her shocked refusal the thought that her life with Geoffrey would be forfeited hadn't come into the equation. Silas had dismissed the other man as unimportant. In her heart of hearts she knew the relationship had gone as far as it ever would. The thought of hurting him added to the burden she bore.

Her last thoughts before a troubled, dream-laden sleep didn't involve either of the men in her life. They were of a little boy in a photograph.

CHAPTER TWO

To ONLOOKERS, they made an eye-catching couple.
Silas was oblivious to the admiring glances cast in their
direction but Rachael felt them without any sense of
pleasure. The familiarity suggested by the light grip on
her arm as they went to board the jet for Heathrow
stood in stark contrast to the emotional chasm that
yawned between them.

She didn't know Silas Tredegar! The knowledge had
come as a shock several weeks earlier; now she wondered how she could ever have fooled herself into
thinking she did. He had taken her life and completely
re-routed it. She had spent her wedding day in a daze,
trying to work out how she had become the centre of a
glittering pageant that was as real as a Hollywood stage
set. When it was over and the photographers had
started to pack away their equipment, she had half
expected them to dismantle the church, so utterly false
did it all seem.

If Silas found the experience strange, he camouflaged
it well. Rachael had begun to hate that cloak of charm
he hid behind. He was an obliging stranger, who
treated her doubts and fears with tolerance, but she
knew she would meet pure granite if she seriously
opposed him. She had already come into collision with
that aspect of his character. When the initial shock of
Silas's proposal had worn off, Rachael had tried to
wriggle out of the trap she was in by trying to secure a
loan to pay off the debt. Silas had neatly intervened,
refusing to allow Personnel to give details of her
income or prospects.

'You could sell the lease to your flat.' He had

surveyed her options with clinical detachment. 'But as far as the legal proceedings are concerned it's one minute to midnight. You certainly won't keep the matter a secret from your parents. Neither will you stop Michael gambling or get him an excellent position with an international company.'

She had considered selling the lease or using it as collateral with the less scrupulous loan sharks until the sale went through. A phone call from her mother had sealed her fate. Michael had been attacked by two unknown assailants and her parents were experiencing a series of unpleasant pranks and acts of petty vandalism.

'What did you expect? Men in pin-striped suits?' Silas had picked up his phone, regarding her with a cynical gleam in his eyes. 'I'd be a fool to give away an advantage like this. Do you want me to put an end to this?'

She had nodded, unable to put her submission into words.

His regard had warmed considerably. 'I think you'll find you've made the right decision. Life will be considerably easier, if you accept doing things my way.'

'For you, I'm sure.' She had found her voice. 'But if you think you're getting a secretary-cum-sleeping-partner, you couldn't be more wrong. You'll get the whole woman, Silas, not the polite, patient version that can escape at five o'clock.'

The prospect hadn't seemed to frighten him. A smile had played around his mouth, as if he found her amusing. 'I don't think either of us fully appreciates what we're getting but I, for one, shall enjoy finding out.'

Cameo scenes from the past month blocked out the polite welcome of the air hostess. Their engagement had been a seven-day wonder at Tredegar and Pitt,

Greta pretending what amounted to clairvoyance about their coming nuptials.

'Ever since Geoffrey came into the frame, he's been like a cat on hot bricks,' she intimated, moving from one cliché to another. 'I thought he'd make a move if he thought he was going to lose you.'

It was one of the many false impressions Rachael had to deal with. Silas had said it; she was the type to make a good wife and mother but not the sort of woman who usually figured in his romances. Knowing this, she found his attempts to promote any intimacy between them embarrassing. It was an awkward situation and one that didn't get any easier as the end of the month approached. Fortunately, the need to tidy up loose ends at the office and brief Silas's new personal assistant kept her mind fully occupied. During the evenings she was busy consulting her mother over wedding plans or accompanying Silas to various functions. It was a busy time, and during her few reflective moments she suspected her fiancé was deliberately leaving her little time to think over their bizarre agreement, but she never challenged him with it; neither did she question her reasons for not doing so.

After an orgy of shopping for Rachael's trousseau, they left the urban sprawl of the seaboard city for the prairie state of Iowa. The contrast amounted to culture shock. Highly conscious of Silas's presence, she became super-sensitive to the marked change in pace. New York days were worked hard and played hard. Life in Iowa was slower; the land demanded time rather than frenetic activity and the day ended more often than not in a lengthy evening meal, sun-drugged tiredness ensuring that conversation lingered rather than sparkled.

Her parents had been amazed at her sudden decision to get married, especially when the prospective bridegroom wasn't the one they had been expecting. They didn't know what to make of Silas. He was a creature from another world, a property tycoon tied into the mystical movement of international finance. He was far too adept at the art of polite conversation and putting people at ease to make her parents feel awkward, but his unscratchability defied any deep insight into his character that might have reassured them. Consequently, Sam and Emily James arrived at their own independent conclusions about their daughter's hasty marriage and Rachael had an uncomfortable time convincing them that her motives for accepting Silas's proposals were the usual ones.

'Is it because of Michael?' her father asked shrewdly, looking up from his work on a tractor that was acting up. Rachael had taken him a jug of cold, homemade lemonade, the day close and warm and cooling drinks essential.

'Michael?' She pretended not to understand him, watching him straighten and push his hair out of his eyes. 'What do you mean?'

He took the lemonade jug, pouring himself a drink, his mouth turning down at the corners. A tall, rangy man, with sandy hair, his face crinkled up when he smiled but when he was serious it contrived to make him look solemn and vunerable at the same time.

'Silas Tredegar,' he breathed out with heavy emphasis, 'isn't your type. Michael owes more money than he's telling and your boss is a city shark and knows a good opportunity when he sees one.' He drank the lemonade, looking away. Rachael could see the tide of colour under his weatherbeaten skin.

'The first day I met Silas, I wanted to marry him.' The twinkle in her eyes belied the seriousness of her tone. 'And as for my type, I'm not sure what that is. After all this time I know Silas very well. Not everyone can be a prairie farmer, Dad, and I don't think I'd make a very good farmer's wife.'

He grunted, casting her a sideways look. Cherry-red

tailored shorts and a loose white cotton T-shirt gave her an elegance that made his dungarees look distinctly country.

'You say he comes from Cornwall?' He sounded as if he was making the best of things. 'Oh, well, I suppose he gets out of those suits sometimes. I've never seen a man with so many clothes.'

She grinned at that, knowing that Sunday best was Sunday best to her father and a collar and a tie during the rest of the week was only to be borne upon extreme sufferance. It had been a carefully balanced exchange, neither wanting to say too much. Rachael didn't like telling her father lies and he restrained his comments in case she was really in love with Silas.

Her mother, however, didn't find the whirlwind romance hard to understand at all. She was totally taken in by all those steamy, intimate looks Silas gave her when he knew they were being watched. So convinced, in fact, that her mother had her own interpretation of their hasty marriage plans. Silas followed Rachael's desperate retreat into her bedroom to regain her composure. He laughed at the reason behind her agitation.

She doesn't know you very well, does she, Rachael?' He leant back against the window frame. 'You won't even let me kiss you.'

She eyed him with undiluted dislike, frowning at his sudden disinclination to meet her eyes, and her previous agitation as nothing compared to the rush of embarrassment at finding his attention distracted by the slip of her cotton shift down over her shoulder to reveal the generous swell of her breast.

'Oh. . .' She dragged the material back over her arm. 'And you wonder why?' she spluttered indignantly. 'Haven't you anything better to do than make fun out of me?'

The playful moue of his mouth wasn't a denial of her

accusation—rather a tease for taking him seriously. Designer jeans and a pale blue cotton shirt with pockets on the breast kitted him out for an afternoon at a country club. The real country was a dusty tractor that her father was trying to fix. No wonder Silas had to amuse himself baiting her.

'Your parents would think it strange if I didn't attempt to get you on your own sometimes.' He sauntered towards the bed where she lounged with her legs curled underneath her.

In a few panicked seconds, she realised how misleading appearances could be. He might be a good-looking clothes-horse but he was dangerous as well, and she visibly shifted back against the headboard as he sat down with his usual cool assurance. It was unnerving being so close to him, especially in her bedroom, on her bed, with only the faint breath of an evening breeze to disturb the drowsy early summer heat.

He held her gaze for interminable seconds, the mellow golden light dappling the room, casting a warm glow over his face and throat. She couldn't deny herself the pleasure of just looking at him. It was a habit she had fallen into during idle moments in the office when he would forget her presence and mull over some knotty business problem, completely unaware of her inspection. Although his accent was pure English, his jet-black hair was a throwback to the Celts. Winged eyebrows exaggerated the startling contrast made by his eyes that were as blue as the sea and seemed to darken dramatically when he was angry or. . . Rachael's heartbeat accelerated wildly when she realised that she wasn't staring at a preoccupied businessman. Nor did her inspection go by unnoticed! It was returned in full measure. A lurking gleam of laughter lit his eyes at her affronted murmur of protest. His dark lashes sweeping upward from the tell-tale pulse at the base of her throat to storm the citadel of her defences. Rachael felt every nerve jar, struck by blue lightning.

'Rachael.' His voice purred over her, a restraining hand curving around her shoulder as she made a move to rise. 'I'm trying to make this easier for you,' he surprised her by saying. 'It will only serve to worry your parents if they think things aren't right between us.' He lightly traced the curve of her shoulder to the delicate hollows of her throat where the blood beat so fiercely, watching her head go back and the nervous flicker of her lashes as his lips parted in a sensual tease that she found hard to ignore.

'I'm sure you're putting on a good enough act. . .' Dear God, was that her voice sounding so disturbed? 'I don't think we need any long sojourns in the bedroom to convince my mother.'

His laughter was soundless but she felt the feathering warmth of his breath against her cheek. 'I'm going to have to find a way of redirecting all that fire; I'm feeling distinctly singed.' He moved closer, an exasperated sigh greeting the swift turn of her head to avoid his kiss which would surely have followed.

'I'm not ready. . .' Her chestnut hair provided a silken shield for her profile but her voice was unsteady. 'I'm just not ready,' she finished lamely, wishing desperately that he would go away.

'All right,' he accepted, feeling her jump as he hooked her hair back behind her ear, revealing the troubled cast of her features. 'I understand. You've built a lot of barriers against me over the years. I know it isn't easy for you to get used to the change in our relationship but try not to be on the defensive so much, hmm?'

So easy to say, so hard to do! And then the call from Geoffrey just before they left for the airport, telling her how Silas had arranged to have him kept out of the way so that Rachael wouldn't be tempted by any second thoughts.

Having denied any relationship with her employer beyond the confines of the office so vehemently to Geoffrey, it had made breaking the news of her engagement doubly difficult. The implications of a tacky secretary-boss affair carried on behind his back had made the sports coach's reaction a mixed one of disappointment and contempt. Rachael had found his accusations extremely wounding and her pale, strained face in the office the next day had sworn witness to the fact. This, it appeared, Silas had taken as enough justification to arrange Geoffrey's removal on a school trip with the head of the Marshall High sports faculty, who happened to be a golfing acquaintance. Silas's response to her outrage had been one of mild surprise. He couldn't understand what he called 'misplaced sentiments' regarding a man who would only continue to disturb her if he was allowed to remain in the near vicinity. Everything was so simple to Silas. He played life as if it were a chess game. Someone threatened his queen; he removed them from the board, regardless of the consequences.

She was aware of him glancing in her direction as the plane became airborne, ignobly aware of his movements as he released his seatbelt and retrieved his briefcase from the pouch it had occupied during take-off. So he was going to work, was he? What a delightful honeymoon—a timely reminder, no doubt, that she was being transported to Cornwall to serve a purpose that had little to do with the relationship between them. Rachael had never believed it was possible for tempers to simmer for hours without release but hers was doing a magnificent job. She almost forgot about her hatred of flying until the plane hit an air pocket and she broke out of her introspective mood, slightly reassured by the unruffled calm of the seasoned flyers.

'Don't let them see you're scared, Rachael.' Her companion spoke without looking up from the file he was studying. 'We don't want another patronising air hostess fussing over you all the way to London.'

'The last thing I'm thinking about is flying,' she lied. 'I don't know how you can sit there. . .' She broke off, too furious to speak, fuming while he capped his pen and closed the folder, irritatingly unaffected by her outburst. 'I'd already promised to marry you. You didn't have to make Geoffrey into a laughing stock.' Her words grew angrier at his sheer implacability. 'I won't have you acting this way, Silas. I'm a human being; I won't be manoeuvred; I——'

'Two brandies.' He smiled at the air hostess who paused by their seats, turning back to her when the woman went to supply their order. 'I wasn't manoeuvring you, Rachael. You've been under a lot of strain recently and——'

'Oh!' Her derisive laugh mocked him. 'You were thinking of me. How strange, I got the distinct impression you were guarding your own interests. Silly of me, I do apologise.'

Rachael was halted from any further invective as the brandy arrived and she watched him smile, unperturbed, knowing without even having to look that the air hostess would be melting under the charm in those eyes.

'Our interests are linked, wouldn't you say?' He continued the conversation easily, handing her a glass. 'I intend to make sure that remains the case. Cheers.' His glass clipped hers and he lifted it to his beautiful mouth, his raised eyebrow inviting her to follow his example.

'I've never met such an. . . Oh!' she gave up, unable to find the words to express herself as his total lack of conscience revealed itself in his refusal to take her seriously.

With a feeling of burning her boats, she sipped her brandy, one ear registering the smooth hum of the aircraft's engine as it sped her miles away from the States to a shadowy future. As her anger abated, her mind found its usual obsession with the space below.

'I hate flying.' She grudgingly shared her fear.

Reaching out casually, he took her hand in his and began to talk to her about his home and the rugged landscape that provided its setting. Rachael's fear of flying provided a much-needed bridge between them. It wasn't until she blinked drowsily and moved to snuggle more comfortably against Silas's shoulder that she realised how much ground had been lost. She half raised her head to move away but long fingers curled around her skull, easing her back against him.

'You're tired. Sleep for a while.' Silas's voice had an unaccustomed huskiness to it that she found strangely compelling. She had little desire to rekindle the dying embers of their argument, and let her lashes close as he instructed, not even emitting a murmur of protest when the fingers that had restrained her moments earlier found new employment in the rhythmic caress of her hair.

Breaking their journey by stopping over in London, they found their first night alone hardly differed from many evenings shared on numerous business trips. Rachael usually shared Silas's opulent lifestyle when they travelled together and his unspoken agreement that she should have her own bedroom merely heightened the sense of unreality that had clung to her throughout her wedding day. The only odd note was struck by the fact that she was treated with equal deference rather than the usual camaraderie shared by support staff to the world's rich and famous. She went to bed over-tired and distinctly troubled, her mind running in endless circles until finally a deep, healing sleep claimed her.

The next morning, she barely spoke at breakfast, too preoccupied with the day ahead and the small boy she would meet at the end of it. Tristan was a child in a photograph, any identity of his own submerged into that of his surrogate father. He was a miniature version of Silas, alone and vulnerable, needing someone to care for him in a way that Silas Tredegar never would. It was a tantalising prospect, almost like looking into the past. Silas had told her that he had lost his mother when he was barely five and that his father, when he was alive, had been too busy with business to play more than a supervisory role in his life. That he identified so strongly with Tristan was underlined by the lengths he was prepared to go to for the child. Rachael received the impression that he had little intention of emulating his father's absentee parenthood and she was slightly taken aback by the unavoidable conclusion that her newly acquired husband had scars that no one else was allowed to see.

'Comfortable?' Silas glanced across at her from the driving seat of the silver-grey Mercedes hired for the journey west.

'Yes,' she answered quietly, aware of the curiosity behind his polite query. 'I think I'm still suffering from jet lag. I'm sorry if I'm not very entertaining.'

His dark lashes narrowed slightly before he responded to the shift of position of the car in front. The motorway was hindered by repair work and leaving London was a slow, protracted process.

'I don't expect you to be entertaining. . .not if you don't want to be.' He spoilt the moment of concern by winking evilly at her. 'But it occurs to me that you might be somewhat apprehensive about your future. If you want to talk about it, maybe I can put your mind at rest.'

Rachael very much doubted it and it showed on her face. 'I don't think the future is anything we can talk about, Silas. Taking one day at a time seems the most advisable course of action.'

He nodded but didn't look pleased by her reply. His expression brought a gleam of amusement to her eyes. The nearest she had ever seen Silas come to dropping the mask he hid behind was during telephone calls to difficult clients. Even when he was disciplining his staff, he rarely showed temper, his cool sarcasm conveying displeasure without any need for histrionics. But occasionally she had caught a fleeting look of intense irritation tighten his jaw and draw his eyebrows together in a dark frown. Her amusement at getting under his skin was short-lived as he changed tack.

'We're not going to get very far if you keep on pushing me away, Rachael.' He leant casually against the steering-wheel, his eyes disturbingly direct. 'Cornwall is my home, Winterbrook my house, but for you everything will be strange, I realise that.' He reached out, his eyes darkening at her response to the light caress that smoothed back a stray strand of chestnut hair from her cheek. 'I thought I knew everything about you.' A slow smile heightened the tension between them. 'Well, apart from. . .'

'You're supposed to be driving,' she pointed out primly, trying not to shiver as his fingers gently traced the contour of her ear.

He laughed, briefly checking the traffic that was uncompromisingly solid. 'We don't seem to be getting very far.' The mockery was unsubtle. 'I can't help thinking we're using the wrong lines of communication.'

'Perhaps some music will help.' She released herself from his lazy inspection, her heart thudding like a bass drum as he continued to watch her, despite her supposed preoccupation with the cassette rack.

Rachael could feel her skin grow hotter as the prolonged silence was punctuated by the sound of her fingers nervously stumbling over cassettes. She grabbed one of them indiscriminately and shoved it into the deck, cursing the fates when heavy metal music blasted into the car.

Silas—with a commendably straight face—turned down the volume, which was brain-numbing, and feigned mild surprise.

'Now I would never have guessed——'

'Shut up,' she returned in a smothered voice.

'You can't hear the words?' he queried, insouciant. 'A little louder, perhaps?'

'Don't you dare!' Her fingers closed over his as he made to turn it up, a giggle hiccuping from her lips. 'You know perfectly well that I hate it.'

He joined in her laughter, his blue eyes warm and affectionate as he ruffled her hair. It was the first moment of real communication between them since the evening when he had proposed. It set the mood for the rest of the journey, allowing them to return to the accord they usually enjoyed during their many hours spent working together. It was a long way from the intimacy shared by newly-weds, but any respite from the tension between them was welcome.

Rachael had used jet lag as an excuse for her preoccupation earlier that day but she found that once relaxed in Silas's company she felt sleepy again. Not that she imagined that the air trip was totally responsible; she had spent a month living on her nerves and it was beginning to take its toll. Consequently she missed the first part of the journey, not waking until they were well into Devon. They had lunch in a pub complete with thatched roof and mock Tudor décor before taking to the road once more for the final leg of their journey.

Much to her surprise, Rachael discovered that she
had taken in some of the information passed on to her
during the flight from New York. She watched fascinated as the scenery changed from the picturesque
Devon villages to a harsher, almost hostile landscape.
She remembered Silas's telling her that most people
considered Cornwall's coastline its most attractive feature; something in his voice suggested that his affection
for the place went deeper than superficial tourist attractions. It must do, she acknowledged, because he was
totally absorbed in it all despite the fact that the sky
had turned the colour of pewter and an aggressive wind
buffeted the car, its attack relentless as they travelled
further west.

A land of granite and slate revealed itself, often
covered in moor or heathland, giving way to steep-
sided valleys, providing a breath of beauty between the
war of the elements and stubborn earth. Cornwall's
climate was reputedly mild but strong winds and lashing
rain had influenced the architecture of low-pitched
roofs and squat, solid churches, swearing testimony to
the force of the Atlantic storms that attacked the
peninsula.

Their destination, Winterbrook House, lay a few
miles south of St Agnes. It had been a farmhouse in
the distant past, but as the Tredegar family had transferred their interests to commerce in Truro and beyond
they had retained the house out of sentimental attachment, selling most of the land to their neighbours.

For the first time it occured to Rachael that Silas had
used the word 'home' when talking of Cornwall.
'Cornwall is my home, Winterbrook my house. . .' The
words came back to her, the possessive ring unmistak-
able. New York had provided his base for as long as
she had worked for him; she had presumed nothing
would change and yet she had snubbed any attempt on

his part to discuss the future. No wonder he had looked puzzled by her attitude!

'Silas——' She was diverted by his sudden sharpening of attention, catching a glimpse of a roof and a chimney before the bend in the road hid the house from sight.

'There it is.' He smiled as if he was greeting an old friend. An old friend whose stern, tough features mellowed through the eyes of love.

Rachael's eyes widened in surprise, visions of Silas's Manhattan apartment and a host of palatial residences hired while abroad on business jarring incongruously with the house now in full view. Grey-slated and granite-faced, it looked impregnable, but it certainly wasn't pretty!

CHAPTER THREE

SILAS brought the Mercedes to a smooth halt outside the house, chalky gravel crunching under the wheels of the limousine. A large raindrop splattered on to the windscreen, followed after a short pause by another.

'It looks as if we're in for a bad night.' Silas's words were almost carried off by the wind as he opened the car door.

Rachael looked out into the gloom and felt the first snagging grasp of wind at her hair as she slid out of the car to stand by his side.

'What do you think?' His eyes smiled but he was watchful. 'You're very quiet.'

She moved nearer to him to shelter in the line of his body. She wasn't fooled; he expected her to be shocked.

'It has a certain bleak charm,' she returned, eyeing him suspiciously. 'Is it equally authentic inside? I feel as if I've been thrown back a couple of centuries.'

He took her elbow and urged her towards the door. 'It needs a complete overhaul. I thought we could plan the décor together.'

Again the presumption that this house was to be their home. Rachael opened her mouth to question his decision when the door opened and she was forced to postpone the discussion by the ensuing round of introductions.

A solidly built woman beamed broadly at them before she embraced the tall, immaculate figure beside Rachael. He stooped, laughing, and kissed the woman's wrinkled cheek.

'You get more beautiful every time I see you,' he greeted her. 'How are you, Kitty? Where's Ted?'

'I told him to put the kettle on; I knew you'd want some tea. I've baked some of your favourite scones.' Kitty's blue eyes were moist as she turned to Rachael. 'Mrs Tredegar.' She held out her hand and the younger woman smiled warmly.

'Please call me Rachael.' She shook hands with the woman, feeling the weak grip and wondering just how old Kitty was. Around seventy, she would guess, and certainly too old to care for such a barn of a house. It was clear from the way her gaze transferred itself almost immediately to Silas that she adored him, and Rachael wearily added another name to his bevy of admirers.

Ted was in the kitchen, a white-haired man with a leathery complexion. He placed a gigantic teapot on to a snowy white tablecloth and his face became wreathed in smiles as Silas moved towards him.

'Good to see you, boy.' He gripped the younger man's arms and Rachael felt strangely tearful.

Silas had always seemed to her a sleek, beautiful creature, essentially solitary by nature. To see him capable of generating and returning such honest warmth shook her more than any of the other changes she had already noticed. It had never occurred to her that his self-sufficiency was just another name for loneliness. So many people flocked to be near him that she hadn't, until then, realised how little permanence his life held.

The sound of unsteady footsteps drew all eyes to the kitchen doorway. Kitty shook her head reprovingly. 'I don't know how he manages to get out of that playpen.' She wagged her finger at the small boy, who giggled, his eyes bright and bold as he moved forward and lifted his arms to Silas, who picked him up and held him high, laughing at Tristan's uncontrollable chuckles.

'Tris, this is. . . I suppose it had better be Mummy. We don't want to confuse him.'

Rachael swallowed drily and nodded. It was the oddest feeling imaginable, taking the wriggling two-year-old from him and trying to make the acquaintance of the boy who was from then onwards to be her son.

'Are you. . .?'

'Daddy, yes.' He tweaked Tristan's nose. 'Kitty and Ted know all the facts but beyond that. . .' He shrugged. 'I'm afraid I'm seen as something of a cad in these parts. It's a storm we'll have to ride.'

'Downright disgraceful of Mr Scott leaving you to get blamed for his mistakes,' Kitty began passionately. 'I hate people thinking you would have done such a thing——'

'All right, Kitty,' Silas cut in firmly. 'It's water under the bridge, hmm?' He shared a long glance with the woman, who nodded sadly and covered up the awkward moment by turning to fuss with the tea things.

They sat around the kitchen table, the warmth from the Aga stove a welcome contrast to the wind that screeched around the house. Rachael allowed the little boy to crawl off her lap on to Silas's. He sat propped in the crook of one arm, his dark head against the pale grey wool of Silas's jacket. It wasn't hard to imagine them father and son; they were so much alike, that it was uncanny.

They chatted with the older couple for about half an hour, Rachael answering questions about her home and promising to show them the wedding photographs as soon as her parents posted them on. Silas did most of the talking, occupying Tristan with a puzzle ring he produced from his pocket, quietening the child in much the same way as he had done Rachael on the plane, stroking the boy's hair until his eyes began to get heavy and his head lolled against his arm.

'You're very good with him.' Rachael didn't try to

hide the admiring note in her voice as she watched him tuck the child into his cot. 'He seems very comfortable with you.'

'Yes.' He straightened, giving her a keen look. 'This rather shallow image you have of me, Rachael—how on earth did you fall in love with it?'

'I didn't,' she protested, backing towards the door as he came after her. 'I told you, I thought you were very attractive but. . .'

'It was just a physical thing?' He raised a dark eyebrow, watching her like a cat with a panicked mouse as her hand stumbled over the doorknob and she continued her retreat into the passage.

'If you like.' Rachael was forced to stop and wait for him as he closed the door quietly. She couldn't run away, there was nowhere to run to, but she was painfully aware of the fact that he would show her to her room next and the conversation was one she would very much like to avoid.

'So why the reticence about sleeping together?' He halted beside her, hands in the pockets of his dark, cord trousers. 'Kissing me, then,' he amended as her eyes skidded away from his.

'It's a. . . Well, I'm a glorified nanny. That's what you want, not a—er—lover.' She tried desperately to keep her voice level, unaware of the revealing nature of her profile and the curious, half disbelieving frown on her husband's face as he saw the vulnerability expressed there.

'You're under some illusion that I can take a woman to bed without actually wanting her?' He gave a short laugh. 'Rachael, I must do something about your low self-esteem.'

'No.' She jerked backwards, only to be caught by the front of her jacket and yanked away from the banister, hearing Silas swear under his breath as he

steadied her. 'I'm sorry.' She raised her lashes tenta-
tively to meet the condemnatory glare of his.
'Would. . .wouldn't it be easier if you'd let me come to
you? I mean, you're always pushing me into corners. I
don't get a chance to relax with you.'

His breathing was still erratic and she could tell by
the awkward movement of his throat that her brush
with near disaster had shaken him a great deal.

'If I could get you in a corner, it might be safer.' He
half smiled but there was a determined look in his eyes
that indicated he didn't think much of her suggestion.
'I'd better show you to the bedroom before you do
anything rash. I promise, on this occasion, to be the
perfect gentleman.'

Rachael felt her hackles rise at the muted sarcasm,
tossing her hair back in a spirited flourish that didn't
escape his attention as he mockingly waved her towards
the next door along from Tristan's.

'This is the only room I've renovated.' Silas ushered
her into the master bedroom. 'I'll sleep in the dressing-
room for the moment; I'd prefer Ted and Kitty to
remain in ignorance about the rather unusual nature of
our marriage,' he replied to the questioning look she
sent him.

Rachael accepted this but still felt uncomfortable at
having him in such close proximity.

The bedroom was a welcome sign of civilisation in
an otherwise old-fashioned house. Silas's grandfather,
the previous occupant, had clearly had a penchant for
the uglier side of Victoriana. Either that or he hadn't
bothered with the expense of new furniture.

The design was exactly right. So perfect in fact that
it was easy just to take pleasure in it without noticing
the thought that had gone into it. Keeping in tune with
the rugged setting of the house, it blended a mixture of
wood and whitewashed brick into a highly imaginative
contrast. The floor was tiled, highly polished and

warmed by huge llama-skin rugs. A fire burned in the
hearth, powered by gas and given an authentic lifelike
appearance by mock logs with the real thing piled in a
neat stack beside it. It was surrounded by the white
brick, an effect that would never have been attempted
if there had been polluting smoke to discolour it.

'Trust you to start with the bedroom,' she murmured, the wide bed with its natural weave cover the
last thing she chose to notice.

'And where would you start, Rachael?' he queried
silkily. 'The cellar?' It was a provoking dig and she did
her best to ignore it.

'The attics, probably.' She ignored the glint in his
eyes. 'That way all the dust doesn't settle on the rooms
you've just decorated.'

'Ah.' He pretended to take her seriously. 'Very
practical. I'll fetch the luggage while you acquaint
yourself with your new surroundings. The bathroom is
through there.' He gestured to a closed door. 'Dinner's
at eight. Rest for a while if you like. It won't take me
long to change and I promise not to disturb you until I
have to.'

'Thank you.' She needed a long soak and some time
to herself more than anything in the world and her
gratitude was genuine.

'Anything to please.' His voice was dry but not
unkind and Rachael's eyes followed him as he left the
room, wondering how many women would appear so
eager to have him leave their bedroom. She was in the
minority, she accepted, and that was part of the
problem. It would be so easy to give herself up to Silas
but what would happen when his attention wandered?
When security for Tristan failed to be a strong enough
reason to bind him to her? How would she cope with
the lies and deceit that would surely follow? She had
no answers to such questions and with a heavy sigh she
eased the weight of hair from her neck, massaging the

tense muscles there, making her way into the bathroom
to enjoy the soothing ministrations of a hot scented
bath.

After tackling the antiquated plumbing system via the
white enamel monstrosity of a bath with great copper
taps that poured a veritable torrent of water, Rachael
had been stumped for evening wear. Finally, she settled
on a smart black cocktail dress with a pencil-line skirt,
matching it with a herringbone jacket she had bought
while still in a sensible economical mood. Upon seeing
her first purchases, Silas had personally escorted her
back to the salons he had recommended, bluntly
informing her that he wanted her to get out of the up-
market Girl Friday image into something distinctly
more glamorous. She didn't know where he had in
mind when encouraging her to buy a host of flimsy
creations but it certainly wasn't Winterbrook.

'I think I look very chic,' she murmured defensively
at the full-length mirror, admiring the black, finely
patterned stockings that gave her appearance a faintly
Parisian air. With an impatient toss of her head she
refused to give her appearance another thought and
went down to dinner early to avoid the possibility of
clashing with Silas when he wanted to change.

The dining-room had a real log fire roaring in the
grate, its orange heart becoming a ferocious sparking
fury when draughts of air knifed at it from dark, chilly
corners of the room. A great chandelier hung over the
table like a frozen shower of crystal tears, sup-
plemented by two Gothic candelabra holding virginal
white candles yet to be lit. The table was a rich
mahogany, reflecting the glass and porcelain table
settings in its satiny sheen, the whole effect reeking of
history in a way Rachael found a little disturbing.

The American tradition was still that of the pioneer;
even the cosmopolitan society Silas moved in mixed

high tech with antiquity in a way that adorned the new rather than paid homage to the old. But here she sensed something more solid, more tenacious. At Winterbrook, Silas's loyalty to his family made sense. And another perception began to take shape that was even stranger. The fact that she was an intruder, not Cornish, not even English, was significant. Why, she didn't know. Fanciful ideas about new blood bubbled in her semi-conscious mind but she dismissed such ramblings as the tattoo of rain against glass drew her to the window, the rattling panes and hiss of sap burning on wood in the hearth making her shiver apprehensively. She almost expected something grotesque to stare back at her instead of the rather troubled image of her own reflection. There was nothing to see out of the window, no lights, just an impenetrable darkness that screeched with the fury of the building storm.

She jumped as the door opened and Silas joined her, her eyes sliding away from the sensual tease in his. She had scorned his girlfriends as a pack of mindless fleabrains; now, joining their ranks, she was beginning to think they didn't stand a chance.

'Emily Brontë must have stayed here.' She tried to shake off her nervousness. 'It's certainly Heathcliff country, isn't it?'

He joined her by the window, his dark suit contrasting with crisp white linen, giving him a smooth, professional look. A faint tang of aftershave drifted to her nostrils and she turned her head to look at him for a second, her gaze lingering on his freshly shaven jaw.

'Heathcliff preferred Yorkshire, but I know what you mean.' He stared out into the darkness. 'After New York I find it rather refreshing.'

As he glanced down at her, his leisurely appraisal made her shift uncomfortably. 'Drawing up the battle lines?' He stroked a finger over the material hugging the ridge of her shoulder. She turned and he blocked her escape with his arm, meeting the angry question in her eyes equably. 'Prim little combinations like this excite the imagination, Rachael; how clever of you to guess that I can never resist a girl in uniform.'

He knew she dressed in a severe, no-nonsense fashion when she was attempting to distance herself from his over-amorous business acquaintances, and clearly saw her choice for the evening in that light.

'It's the warmest thing I've got for evening wear.' She fingered the lapel of the jacket, looking down at the classic simplicity of the garment. 'I'm sorry if you disapprove.'

Lifting her eyes to his face, she discovered he wasn't in the least interested in her explanation. His appreciative inspection took in every detail of her appearance from her elegant high-heeled shoes to the burnished crown of her chestnut hair.

'I have the feeling,' he spoke in soft whimsical tones, 'that I missed the scene where I should have taken off your glasses and said in awed wonder, "Why, Miss James, but you're beautiful."' A smile came into his eyes at Rachael's feigned boredom. 'But then you're quite determined to resist my much-vaunted charm, aren't you, Rachael? And, although you don't need spectacles, I suspect you're peculiarly blind to your own attractions.'

The way he spoke and looked at her would make any woman feel like a million dollars, Rachael acknowledged, dampening down the leap of exhilaration that threatened to cloud her mind. It was a difficult task. The slightest movement by either of them would bring them into contact, and it took all of her will-power to maintain the distance.

'You seem to have found it easy enough to resist me until now,' she pointed out, wishing her voice sounded cool and crisp instead of husky and disturbed. 'And you promised to let me have enough time. . .'

'To get used to living with me,' he agreed, his lazy perusal of her face forgotten for a moment as he met the resentment in her dark eyes, an equal amount of grit behind the playfulness in his. 'I'm beginning to think I could wait forever. Even the shyest couples would have managed some degree of intimacy within a month. All I'm asking is that you don't scuttle away like a frightened rabbit every time I come near you, nor regard our relationship as some kind of rubber stamp ensuring both Tristan's and Michael's well-being. I think, in the circumstances, we owe ourselves a little more than that.'

Silas waited for an answer, impatience firming his lips as she hesitated in reply. The sound of the trolley being pushed down the hallway gave her a much-needed reprieve, but the exasperated sigh from Silas left her in little doubt that he didn't welcome the intrusion. He removed the arm that had barred her way, his displeasure plain to see.

'Saved by the Exeter stew,' he mocked, indicating that she should take the opposite end of the table while he moved to open the door for Ted.

It was clearly an effort for the older man to manoeuvre the trolley into the room, the fact highlighted by the smoothness of the operation once Silas took charge. Kitty followed her husband, insisting on serving the meal despite Rachael's assurance that they could manage themselves.

'Just how long have Ted and Kitty been here?' She voiced the question as soon as the elderly couple had closed the door and were out of earshot.

'Their whole working lives, I should imagine.' He lifted his wine glass in a brief salute, choosing not to hear the note of accusation in her voice. 'They know more about the family history than I do; they'll be delighted to tell you all the old tales if you ask them.'

'I'm sure they would, but you know very well that isn't what I meant.' She picked up her fork, suppressing a terrible desire to throw it at him when he continued to play cat and mouse with her.

'Don't you like them? I know they're inclined to fuss, but——'

'They're too old to continue running a place like this!' Her temper unravelled at his deliberate obtuseness. 'Ted had to use both hands to lift the teapot earlier and letting him wheel that trolley fully loaded up the hallway is inviting disaster. I know you're inclined to let your staff merge in with the wallpaper, but——'

'That's enough, Rachael,' he cut in quietly, but with sufficient force to bring about the result he required. 'For your information, I intend to increase the staff now we've taken up residence, but I can't leave them without anything to do; they wouldn't take charity.'

'It wouldn't be charity, surely? They must have pensions,' she persisted with terrier-like tenacity. It was a doomed battle; she knew in her heart of hearts that Silas genuinely cared for the old couple and that her concern was exacerbated by the emotional tumult building inside her.

'They have,' he agreed icily. 'They chose to continue living here in preference to a bungalow in Truro. They cooked this meal because they're my friends and they wanted to welcome us to Winterbrook, not because I cracked a whip over their tired old bones. I assure you, they're under no obligation whatsoever to wait on me.'

Cold blue fire chilled Rachael to the marrow. As his secretary, her efficiency had always kept her on the right side of her employer; she had shivered when he used that tone to those that displeased him and she didn't find it any more palatable when it was directed at her.

'I'm sorry.' Her apology was a little shame-faced. 'I. . .' She prodded at a piece of steak on her place. 'In the office it always seemed——'

'We're not in the office now,' he pointed out with stark emphasis. 'Running a large company demands many things. I doubt if most of my staff would appreciate a bleeding heart in preference to an image of assured success. The fact that you wanted something more from me. . .' he imprisoned her gaze with his '. . .is something entirely different.'

That shocked her slightly, and the sudden recognition of the truth of his words lay naked for him to see. Rachael wanted to close her eyes and shut out that sharp, analytical stare, but the power he exuded was mesmeric.

'I haven't changed your job title from secretary to nanny. I want a wife and all that entails.' His tone was light again, like the swish of a rapier slicing through air. 'Forgive me if I'm wrong, but I think you see your body as a battlefield. It's a rather old-fashioned interpretation of the war between the sexes; most women these days have a far more positive attitude towards sex.'

'I haven't noticed many winners coming out of your stable.' She regained some of her fire and saw the glimmer of appreciative amusement warm his eyes.

'That's debatable. But doesn't it occur to you that I've made sure you weren't a loser for three long years? True, I could have had you, especially when you came fresh and dewy-eyed from the country, but then I knew I would lose you and that proved a considerable deterrent.' He laughed at the look she sent him, catching his lower lip between predatory white teeth and shaking his head with a mixture of admiration and impatience. 'You should listen to Greta's version of our romance. It has seeds of truth among the candy-floss; she's a shrewd lady, which is more than I can say for you.'

'I'm sorry I'm such a disappointment,' she muttered under her breath, the flames from the decorative candles revealing the sheen of tears in her eyes. She was tired of fighting him but unable to give in. He was right; she did see her body as a battlefield—it was the only thing she had denied him through the years. It had been a matter of pride to remain one of the unconquered women in his life. If she gave in, what would she be? Just another notch on his bedpost!

'So defensive,' he mocked, cruelly cajoling her into a response even if it was just temper. 'Does the thought of making love always have this effect or is it just me?'

'Can't we eat dinner in silence?' she asked stiffly. 'You're giving me indigestion.'

He pulled a face of mock penitence. 'You know I can't stand it when you go silent on me.'

'Well, stop it, then.'

'Stop what?'

'Being such a perceptive man.' She threw down her serviette. 'I didn't think you'd have to ask.' Eyes flashing furiously, she pushed back her chair and marched to the door. She almost ran when she heard him behind her and fought him as he pulled her into his arms. When she tried to wriggle away, he merely held her closer.

'Shush.' He placed a gentle kiss against her temple. 'There's nothing to be frightened of, Rachael; I'm not going to hurt you.' A hint of curiosity entwined with the soothing tone of his voice. 'I know my—er—lady friends had a habit of pouring their woes into your ear, but if any of them ever said——'

'No.' She gave a shaky little laugh, feeling the cool silk of his tie against her cheek and breathing in the musky, masculine scent through the crisp linen of his shirt. 'No, they didn't complain about the way you treated them, more the brevity of the relationship. . .'

It was a dead giveaway but she ceased to care; he might as well know she didn't trust him—he was bound to find out sooner or later.

'I see.' His hand stroked over her hair and she could sense that he was choosing his words carefully. 'You think I'd behave that way towards you?'

Rachael lifted her head and he read the confirmation in her eyes, frowning slightly as she managed to look proud and vulnerable at the same time.

'No relationship is without a degree of risk. You can't play safe all your life, Rachael. I know, I've done it for a long time and it bores me.'

'And you're breaking out with me?' She couldn't keep the disbelief from her voice and he bent his head and kissed her cheek, pausing over her mouth.

'Why not? I care more about you than any of the women I've taken to bed. I can't think of anyone I'd rather wake up beside. That's rather frightening for an emotional coward like me.' He smiled, his eyes serious and slightly self-deprecatory. 'Now, do you think we could finish the meal? I haven't much of an appetite, but Ted and Kitty will be hurt if we leave it untouched.'

'Yes.' Her mouth was stiff, mesmerised by the firm, well-chiselled lips inches from hers. He was conscious of the proximity as well, and a heavy, charged silence fell between them, disturbed only by the rattle of rain against the window. The lights flickered momentarily and with an inarticulate murmur Silas closed the gap between them, his arms tightening around her slender body, his mouth seeking the softness of hers.

It became stunningly clear what had frightened her the moment their lips met. She had kept herself for him. Had lived through the turmoil of moving from a claustrophobic country life to the big city without becoming prey to the first wolf that came along because her wolf had, for his own reasons, left her alone. And now all the passionate hunger she had subdued and even come to believe she didn't possess surged through her veins with the force of a river breaking its dam.

Their first kiss began gently, almost as if he was letting her get used to the touch of his mouth. The seconds drew out endlessly as the brush of his lips became increasingly insistent. That it was Silas holding her, his breath tickling her skin, caused tiny rockets of feeling to shoot through her body, exploding in a cascade of sensation that was hot, prickly and like ice on her skin all at the same time. The delicate inner skin of her lower lip felt the tip of his tongue run like a finger of fire across its surface. Rachael's breath shuddered in her throat; her eyes frayed open to catch a glimpse of the white candles, flames quivering. Silas was a blur of warm brown skin and jet black hair. Closing her eyes as if drugged, she felt his hands splay against her back to gather her to him and mindlessly parted her lips at his softly spoken request.

Oh, God, her heart quaked, her hands moving against him in a sudden desire to be free as his mouth firmly took hers and his tongue leisurely plundered the soft well within. It was a mystery to Rachael how he managed to deflect her bid to escape and her arms ended up around his neck, leaving him free to slide his hands down to her hips and mould her against him, his fingers insidiously smoothing the black material of her skirt, appreciating the outline of her buttocks and drawing her hard against him in a way that drew the final curtain on their previous relationship in a way words never could.

'Silas!' She tore her mouth from his, outrage leaping from her eyes which his slow, knowing smile did nothing to ease, nor the fact that he had failed to increase the distance between them.

'Geoffrey must have ice in his veins. Either that or more patience than most males would wish to possess.'

'Why, you. . .!' A strangled sound broke from her throat and Silas caught her wrists, muffling an oath when her toe caught his ankle.

'You're certainly an old-fashioned girl, considering you pack quite a punch for an amateur.' He laughed at her speechless fury, forcing her hands behind her back so that she couldn't attempt to do what her eyes were threatening. 'I promise, saving yourself for me is definitely one of your better decisions.'

'In a pig's eye,' she retorted rudely, distressed by how much she had given away. She could only return the pleased, self-satisfied smile with a stormy glare. Her hair had become tumbled into a tangled chestnut fury, giving clear testimony to the temper usually kept under firm control. 'Get off me!' She spoke each word succinctly.

He released her imprisoned hands, catching her right one as it made to slap him across the face. Blue eyes glittered with malicious humour.

'I have to know these things, Rachael.' He watched the hectic colour come into her cheeks, fully aware of her sensitivity on such subjects and needling her unmercifully. 'Your unwillingness to communicate means I have to use dynamite to make any progress at all. When you're a little more forthcoming, our relationship should become easier. Though, I must admit. . .' He raised her captured hand to his lips, his eyes saying the rest for him.

Rachael snatched her fingers free, the light brush of his mouth tingling over her skin, moving away as sounds were emitted once more from the hallway. Silas followed her back to the table, his relaxed manner at total odds with her hurried steps. It was always the same; she got all hot and bothered while he stayed as cool as the proverbial cucumber.

'Tidy your hair, my dear; you look rather tousled.'
He picked up his wine glass, clearly enjoying the
emotional fireworks generated between them.

The haughty chill in her eyes was met by another
burst of soft laughter and Kitty gave them both a
pleased smile, no doubt thinking they were indulging
in the happy banter of newly-weds.

The evening seemed to fly past after that, Kitty
serving them with fruit and cheese followed by coffee.
She came back to clear away, despite Rachael's offer
to lend a hand.

'Why don't you get ready for bed, darling?' Silas
interceded smoothly. 'I'll help Kitty.' He winked at the
elderly woman. 'It will give me a chance to catch up on
all the gossip.'

Kitty chuckled delightedly, willing, it appeared to
accept Silas's offer even though she grumbled good-
humouredly about him being more trouble than he was
worth. With their last skirmish in mind Rachael totally
agreed with that assessment of his character, flicking
him a disdainful glance before leaving them to it. She
would have liked to close the day with a minor victory,
but his intimately spoken, 'I won't be long, sweetheart,'
flung her back into panic and she almost ran up the
stairs to the bedroom, feeling a complete and utter
idiot when she realised there was to be no sanctuary
there. To get to the dressing-room he had to have
access to the master bedroom and it was with measured
relief that she found the bathroom door was at least
lockable. She changed in there, scrambling into bed,
hoping that he would assume she was asleep when he
came upstairs and leave her alone. If he didn't, she
swore vehemently, he'd have a fight on his hands.

It was almost an anticlimax when he finally came.
She heard the door to the next room open and realised
that he must be looking in on Tristan. That unsettled
her, reminding her of the more admirable qualities she

had discovered since coming to Winterbrook. To make it worse, he entered the room quietly, switching off the subdued wall lights, and whether he was aware of the tense curl of her body or not his only attempt to touch her was to place a light kiss on her cheek. He didn't speak and Rachael listened to the sounds of him moving away to the dressing-room with a surge of remorse.

'I could at least have said goodnight,' she whispered into the pillow, a lone tear dampening the cheek he had kissed. If only he hadn't been so aggravating about her lack of experience. Virginity! She stopped avoiding the issue. She had a presentiment that making love with Silas was going to be nothing short of cataclysmic, and viewed the prospect of being totally defenceless against him with a sick feeling of apprehension. Surprisingly enough, her plight wasn't the last thing on her mind before she went to sleep. Instead, a vague curiosity lurked as she remembered Silas's response to her closeness.

'He does want me,' she murmured as her eyelids drooped closed. She fell into sleep, her mouth curving into a soft smile.

CHAPTER FOUR

RACHAEL crouched down, staring into a relatively still pool of water created by erosion from the burst of spring rains. The drier weather reduced the flow to a trickling brook that gave Winterbrook House its name. Small fish shot in all directions as a net disturbed their peaceful habitat. Tristan giggled uproariously, more intrested in the splash than in trying to catch any of the disturbed inhabitants.

'I think you need a more physical sport.' She laughed at the duffled figure, an arm around his waist as he created another tidal wave.

'It runs in the family.' A voice spoke from above her and she looked up, startled, to see a man watching them both with a sombre expression. 'You must be Rachael.' He came down the bank with an expertise that suggested he was used to the rough terrain. 'I'm Scott Tredegar.' He held out his hand and she met the gesture of greeting, having already guessed his identity.

The Tredegars were certainly a distinctive lot. Scott was a roughly hewn copy of Silas, lines of sorrow and a network of hardly visible scars destroying the smooth male beauty that her husband possessed.

'Silas is entertaining my wife,' he intimated, his grip firm. 'So I thought I'd repay the favour.' Blue eyes assessed her, a bitter light making them alien despite the similarity in colour to his cousin's. 'You seem to be getting on very well with Tris.' He released her hand, stooping to pick up the small boy and pretending to bite at Tristan's snubbed nose.

Rachael watched them together with the same sadness she had seen on Scott Tredegar's face when she had first become aware of his presence. Tristan was too busy placing his hands over his nose and trying a similar, unwieldy assault on his aggressor to notice any restraint in his adult playmates.

Laughter made Scott look younger and Rachael couldn't help joining in when Tristan was rather successful in an attack, leaving his real father rubbing his nose ruefully.

'It's hard to explain the rules of play to a child.' He replaced the two-year-old on the ground, straightening and giving Rachael a penetrating glance. 'You're not quite what I expected.' He pushed his hands into the pockets of his sheepskin coat, the wind raking back his black hair, which was shaggy and longer than Silas's, making him look artistic. 'I'm glad. I had a horrible feeling my dear cousin was going to marry some insipid creature and make me feel eternally guilty.'

Scott took a packet of sweets out of his pocket and peeled back the wrapper, popping one of the pastilles into Tristan's eager mouth and offering Rachael one with a mocking grin.

'No, thanks.' She looked up at the sky to escape his stare. 'I was told Cornwall was England's Riviera. Do you think it's a lie put about by the tourist board?' she commented lightly, trying to avoid the undercurrents she sensed but didn't fully understand.

He cast a glance at the darkening sky and fell into step beside her as she urged Tristan back across the stream. 'They have palm trees in Newquay.' He grinned. 'Wait until we have one of those breathless summer days. You've had a bit of a rough introduction—the wind can't keep this up forever.' He took Tristan's free hand, allowing him to jump across the brook. 'Mind if I come back to the house? The walk from Thornfield is enough to chill an Eskimo.'

'No, I don't mind,' Rachael replied warily, wishing Silas had been a little more informative when it came to his family. She had noted the way Scott talked about his cousin and she guessed that they weren't the best of friends despite the sacrifice made on Tristan's behalf.

Winterbrook looked more inviting when the rain came down about two hundred yards from the house and they ran for cover, Tristan hoisted up on Scott's back. With a feeling that she was getting involved in something she would regret, Rachael fetched two towels, throwing one to the man and then going down on to her haunches and drying Tristan's wet hair.

A week in Cornwall had been spent almost exclusively in the child's company. Silas had disappeared to London the day after they arrived, to sort out some problem with a leisure complex Tredegar and Pitt were involved with. That he should visit his cousin's wife before coming home struck her as odd but she was too churned up by meeting Scott and the fact that Silas was back to ponder on it for long.

Tris obediently allowed her to take off his duffle coat and bright red wellingtons, while Scott proved his familiarity with the kitchen and began to make coffee.

'I guess, being a Yank, you prefer caffeine to tannin poisoning.' He put a mug near to her on the table, putting some milk in a plastic beaker for his son. 'How do you like Cornwall? You used to be Silas's secretary, didn't you? That's quite a high-powered job for a woman. Don't you find this place a bit isolated after New York?'

'I was born in the country,' she offered, ignoring the sexist implications behind his comments. 'And I've been busy sorting through the house and looking after Tristan. I really haven't had time to get bored.'

Scott laughed, a grating, unpleasant sound that brought to mind, by contrast, the soft laughter Silas teased her with. The older man had been to hell and back and it showed.

'He must be slipping.' Harsh blue eyes flicked her a

cunning glance. 'I thought Silas's women all pined if he left their sight. And this is supposed to be your honeymoon.'

She sat Tristan on a chair, taking off her coat and pushing a hand through her rain-darkened hair. 'I know how busy he is.' She picked up her coffee, returning his interrogatory gaze calmly. 'And honeymoons are a bit old-fashioned these days, aren't they? I expect we'll take a holiday somewhere warm sooner or later. At the moment. . .' she shrugged expressively '. . .there's a lot to sort out here.'

Scott took a mouthful of coffee, nodding acknowledgement as if chalking up a point to her. 'Definitely not what I expected.' He cocked his head at the sound of tyres sending up gravel in the drive. 'Mandy must be losing her charms; only two hours.' He consulted his watch and then looked towards the kitchen doorway as Silas paused for a moment and then came in to join them with a pantherish grace of movement that made the hairs on Rachael's neck prickle.

'Scott,' he acknowledged grimly, his mouth straight, and she could almost hear his teeth grind, the black wool coat he wore over a pin-striped suit emphasising his city slickness compared to the rougher image preferred by his cousin. 'I thought we had an appointment. I don't find it amusing wasting my time at Thornfield while you are here.'

He ignored Tristan's outstretched hands, glancing down at Rachael, who was busily trying to comfort the child; Tris was getting fractious at the lack of attention.

'You're wet.' He tucked a strand of damp hair behind her ear, letting the back of his finger stroke over her cheek. 'Doesn't anybody bother answering the phone in this place? I've been trying to get through all morning.'

'The line's faulty.' She was aware of the intensity of interest coming from the other side of the table. 'And

Tris and I have been fishing in Winterbrook.' She met Silas's brief kiss, wanting to reassure him without knowing why. 'That's when I met Scott. He was walking on the moors.'

'Oh. . .walking?' Silas ruffled Tristan's hair idly. 'It must be a first for you, travelling under a hundred miles an hour. I can only hope this is a sign of things to come.'

Scott placed his mug down on the table with a grinding motion. 'Something has got under your skin, hasn't it, old son? Or is Winterbrook finally rubbing off the polish? Be careful, Rachael; heaven knows what will happen to such a civilised soul as Silas if he starts getting primitive.'

Rachael was finding the possibility less implausible by the second, but her husband was a master game player. He merely laughed, the tension melting away like a snowflake in June.

'If that unlikely event ever happens, I'd advise you to get out of the way, old son.' He copied his cousin's banter with much greater finesse. It didn't even sound like a threat.

'Would you like something to drink?' Rachael broke into the duel, her fingers unconsciously stroking over Silas's sleeve. He covered her hand with his, turning his head to brush a kiss over her forehead.

'Tris looks tired,' he murmured against her skin. 'And you need to get dry. I have to speak to Scott about some business matters. Could you give me half an hour, darling? Then I'm all yours.'

She accepted that the last part of his reply was for his cousin's benefit. He wasn't in a teasing mood. Despite losing the edge of irritation he had shown earlier, she would place bets on the fact that he was annoyed about something.

'Say goodbye to. . .' Rachael paused, not knowing what to say.

'Uncle Scott,' Silas's cousin supplied, with a bitter twist to his mouth.

Rachael picked up the two-year-old who was, as Silas had predicted, yawning widely. She cast a swift glance at her husband, whose enigmatic profile gave away nothing. It was hard to judge whether he was moved by his cousin's plight or jealous over Scott's claim to Tristan.

'What a mess.' She hugged the little boy protectively as she carried him up the stairs. Silas's adopting his cousin's child seemed a mighty complicated way of solving the problem of his illegitimacy. Surely it would be better for Scott to come clean to his wife? Reading between the lines, she gathered that Amanda Tredegar was the reason for the secrecy and that it went a lot deeper than protecting her against the natural feeling of betrayal and pain any wife would feel upon such a discovery.

'Daddy,' Tristan repeated proudly over and over again as she avoided his flailing legs and pinned a nappy on him. He was still inclined to have 'accidents' during his afternoon nap and at night but as their week together had progressed Rachael detected an improvement and put his lapses down to insecurity rather than inadequate training.

'Yes, Daddy's here,' she agreed wryly, pulling the miniature duvet over him, watching his fingers make waves for the brightly coloured boats printed on the cover.

Tristan's eyes were over-bright and she followed what had become a ritual during the week, telling him about anything that came to mind, knowing it was the sound of her voice and its changing modulation that he followed and finally fell asleep to rather than the content of the conversation. She smiled as his dark lashes eventually fanned his flushed cheeks and, getting up carefully, she tiptoed out of the room.

Her hair had become a mass of small waves as it dried without the aid of a hair-dryer. If it had been a shade redder, her creamy complexion would have made her a dead ringer for a pre-Raphaelite heroine. She entered her bedroom, pulling a face at the mirror. Her appearance just stopped short of being distinctive. Attractive. . .pleasant. . .nice-looking had been as far as the accolades went. It had never bothered her in the past but the Tredegars—and she put them in the plural now—had the tendency to occupy centre stage without even trying. She had yet to meet Mandy but from what she had already gleaned she expected a delicate, exquisite beauty who would make her feel even more like an extra in a cast of stars than she did already.

'Rachael!' She heard Silas call from below and, brushing down her cords and Aran jumper, she decided to meet him on neutral territory rather than have him come upstairs to find her.

'I've just got Tristan off to sleep,' she chided as she arrived, slightly breathless, at the bottom of the stairs, trying to steady her breathing so that he wouldn't guess how desperately afraid she was of being involved in an intimate situation with him.

'Sorry, I didn't think.' He rubbed a hand around the back of his neck, tilting his head back wearily. 'I suppose he was excited at seeing Scott; they have a certain rapport that makes you wonder about all this business about environment over genes.' His eyes moved restlessly over her face as he spoke. 'Is this the first time he's been here? Mandy said you hadn't met yet but my cousin isn't the type to wait for an invitation.'

'He hasn't been here before today.' She glanced past him to the door of the study which she had made her own during his week's absence. It had the advantage of a massive hearth and was one of the few rooms that appeared to have windows that fitted. 'There's a fire in the study. Are you cold? You haven't taken your coat off yet. Or aren't you staying?' The question was mischievous but his smile was a facsimile of the real thing and disturbed her more than any of Scott's tempestuous mannerisms.

'Oh, I'm staying all right.' He followed her to the door, tall, lean and vaguely menacing. 'Winterbrook is my house and so is everything in it. I hope that doesn't take too long to sink in, otherwise we're going to have problems.'

'Silas?' She questioned his advance towards her, her fingers entwining and then splaying out defensively as he reached for her. A hot burn of resentment steadied her nerves and her fingertips rested against his waistcoat, not pushing him away, just trying to calm them both before they were plunged into another one of their frequent rows. 'Don't you think you should let me in on the family feud or whatever it is between you and Scott that has you at each other's throats the second you meet? Don't deny it!' She saw the shuttered look that smoothed out any sign of temper from his well-cut features, pursuing her intuition recklessly. 'I'm not being party to a tug of war with Tristan in the middle of it without a very good reason. I mean it, Silas; I don't care if I am in hock to you——'

'In what?' He lifted a dark eyebrow, watching her mouth firm stubbornly, a hint of the old charm resurfacing.

'Debt.' Her eyes flickered downwards as his hands moved to span her waist. 'And you might as well know now—I refuse to be distracted.' Her voice rose as he squeezed her deliberately, laughing low in his throat at her outraged squeak.

'I'm glad you think it's a possibility,' he murmured, looking terribly handsome, his black hair gleaming in the firelight, his blue eyes warming considerably, a fact that made her expel her breath with relief. For some inexplicable reason, she reached up on tiptoe to kiss him. Obligingly, he held her closer, bending his head to meet her lips gently, this time not attempting to push her any further than she wanted to go.

'You're as slippery as an eel.' She tried to recover from the emotionalism that made her want to laugh and cry at the same time. 'When you put on that public expression you make me want to smash things.'

'Oh.' It was a silent, teasing movement of his mouth. 'I rather like the way you smash things.' He kissed the tip of her nose before releasing her to take off his black wool coat, his movements stiff, and she was quick to help him, holding it for him while he released his other arm.

Glancing around the room, he admired the changes Rachael's touch had brought. The study, he had thought, needed gutting and starting again but the nineteenth-century Bessarabian rug and massive couch had possibilities even if the wooden panelling was irretrievable. It gave the study a dark, brooding air that hinted at rainy days rather than the pleasure to be had, reading in pleasant surroundings. A display of wild flowers in a blue and grey glazed jug, a book open on a dark walnut table and a haphazard sprawl of glossy magazines in front of the fire gave it a lived-in look.

'What would you like to drink?' Rachael folded his coat, the fading warmth of his body and the tang of cologne bringing a rush of awareness that she tried to vanquish.

'Whisky.' He took up a lounging position on the couch, his usual elegance disturbed by a more powerful image of sprawling masculinity. 'Make it a large one; the family skeletons demand some form of anaesthesia.'

She obeyed, surprised at the ease of her victory. When she had first asked him to tell her about the animosity between himself and Scott she had thought he was going to pass it off as irritation at being made to waste his time.

Handing him a chunky glass, half full of the golden liquid, she knelt beside the couch, waiting for him to begin. Silas studied her over the rim of the glass, taking a swallow of the whisky and then closing his eyes as it slid down his throat.

'You look like Tristan waiting to be told a story,' he muttered, half to himself, shifting to get more comfortable against the floral cushions. 'You're a heartless woman interrogating me like this, after I've driven since dawn to get back to you.'

'It takes this long, does it?' She glanced pointedly at her watch and he smiled, reaching out for her hand, which she allowed him to take.

Being at Winterbrook had given her a new insight into her husband's character. The charming rogue she had thought she knew had unsuspected depths and, whereas she could resist the rascal, the new, more complex Silas had a magic all of his own. She had missed him, she admitted reluctantly, and the protective instincts aroused during his skirmish with Scott had opened the floodgates for a whole gamut of emotions. She wanted to touch him and her heart leapt treacherously in her breast as he invited her to do so.

'Just there.' He placed her hand at the side of his neck, urging her to ease the tension there, freeing his tie when she did as he asked. Luckily Silas was too preoccupied by what he had to tell her to notice the change in her.

'I wanted to get rid of business matters first. Scott is hopeless with money. I invest it for him and then he wreaks havoc by spending a fortune on a whim and signing any kind of agreement to get his hands on the cash. Trying to explain long-term capital investment to him is like expecting Tris to understand Einstein's theory of relativity.' He laughed cynically. 'So the artistic nature, ill suited to poverty but possessing in-built contempt for pen pushers.'

He drank his whisky as if it were water and he despised it. Rachael watched him carefully, her fingers straying under the hair that fringed his collar, uncon-sciously imbuing her touch with something dangerously like sensuality.

'What does he do exactly?' she asked quietly, red-dening guiltily at his sharp look, realising she was stroking his hair.

'He runs a couple of craft shops, mainly with an eye to fleecing rich American tourists. He also does a masterly self-portrait in angst, so if you want a cut price-Heathcliff Scott's your man.' His sarcasm was scathing and Rachael drew back from him as if stung.

'That's not very kind, Silas.' She was surprised by his sudden attack. 'I've only talked to Scott for an hour but it's plain to see that he isn't happy. I don't think that qualifies as an adolescent craving for a tragic lover. I'm involved—you involved me—and I don't want to put my foot in it because of ignorance of what goes on here.'

His cool regard exasperated her and she turned her head away in a sudden gesture of defeat, her eyes dark and stormy when he put a finger under her chin and turned her back to face him.

'You're right.' He remained uncontrite. 'Scott is unhappy. Very unhappy. Unfortunately, his misery and guilt have a nasty habit of becoming infectious.' His thumb drew a line under her lower lip but there was no sign of desire in his eyes as he followed the movement. 'Four years ago he developed a taste for fast cars.' His hand moved to cup her cheek, almost as if he needed the distraction. 'He smashed up a very expensive Ferrari and unfortunately his wife was in the car at the time. Now she can't have children and Scott's remorse is so strong that he can't touch the woman he's supposed to love.' Blue eyes were dead to feeling as they met hers. 'Barren and undesired—not an enviable result of someone else's carelessness, and then of course Scott goes one better and expiates all the pent-up frustration on a Mandy lookalike, resulting in Tristan and a heartbroken girl, barely out of her teens, who was busily starving herself to death before she walked in front of a bus, too weak to avoid it.'

He softened slightly when he saw her face whiten. 'I don't intend that Tristan should be added to the casualty figures, nor you for that matter. So you may ask as many questions as you like about Scott but if you blush when you ask them don't expect me to take it lightly.'

'I didn't. . . I mean, not because. . .' Lord, how did she get out of that one? Tell him she had been embarrassed because she thought he was aware of her desire to touch him? Fortunately the sound of the phone ringing in the hall distracted Silas from her stumbling explanation.

'I'll get it.' He stayed her, his long form unwinding from the couch with an agility that denied the signs of exhaustion minutes before.

It was probably for him, she acknowledged, a sudden sense of isolation sweeping over her. All her family and friends were on another continent and at Winterbrook that might as well be as far away as the moon.

Silas returned after a few minutes, leaning against the door-jamb, taking in the lost figure curled up on the couch he had recently vacated.

'Kitty,' he informed her with a faint touch of exas-peration. 'It seems that Ted misread the timetable for the buses and they're stuck in Truro. I said I'd pick them up.' His amused grin had an infectious quality to it and her lips tilted in response. 'I suggested a taxi but

they'd rather walk than be robbed by those bandits.'
he imitated Kitty's Cornish lilt to perfection.

Rachael chuckled. 'Do you want me to fetch them?
You've been driving most of the morning——' He was
already shaking his head and she had vague recollec-
tions of his criticism where her driving was concerned
in the past.

'No, it would take too long to explain where to find
them. I'm going to have a bath and change of clothes
first. They're at Kitty's sister's, so there's no rush. I
thought we'd eat out tonight.' He didn't wait for her to
give her opinion one way or another. 'That way we can
avoid putting pressure on the old family retainers and
you can experiment with your wardrobe.'

Rachael could have happily thrown a whole tea set
at him but he was gone before the cushion that came
to hand hit the door and she heard his laughter echoing
down the hallway.

He did it deliberately, Rachael seethed. A conversation with Silas was like an obstacle course with 'time
out' to recover her breath. That last crack had brought
back the memories of their first evening at Winterbrook
with astonishing vividness, reminding her that they still
had unfinished business between them and that Tristan
and the problems of his paternity were not the only
demands to be made of their marriage. Silas didn't
intend that she should forget that. As if she could! She
only had to look at him. . .hear his voice.

Groaning, she pushed herself to her feet, desperate
for something to do to take her mind off Silas and the
Tredegar family. She usually tried to read when Tristan
was sleeping and her choice of literature consisted of
factual books about the area or local legends and tales.
Picking up one she had started to read the day before,
she curled up on the couch, propping her head up with
her hand, and tried to concentrate on a description of
Tintagel castle.

Later that evening, Rachael left the warm sanctuary of the master bedroom, walking the length of the draughty passageway, vaguely conscious that the earlier lashing rain had given way to wind just short of gale force. It suited her mood. On their first evening together in Winterbrook, her husband's presence in the bedroom had been kept to the minimum; tonight he had made little attempt to keep out of the way. She had sat in mutinous silence on the bed while he wandered about dressed only in his trousers. It occurred to her that he was enjoying her discomfort, but his usual teasing manner was absent. When their eyes met she had blushed like a schoolgirl suffering from a desperate crush. He hadn't commented on the incident, merely looked away and picked up his shirt. Rachael had fled into the bathroom, closing the door behind her, leaning against it, her heart thudding like a bass drum. It was with a growing sense of danger that she steeled herself to face a further encounter, her hand tightening in a brief nervous spasm on the banister as she saw Silas waiting for her at the foot of the stairs.

He glanced at his watch before casting her an assessing look. She lifted her chin, aggressive sexuality, enhanced by the laced-back dress in black denim that moulded her hips and stopped short several inches above the knee. The jacket was slung over her shoulder, and black silk stockings and chunky jewellery in jet and silver completed the outfit. Reaching the bottom of the stair, she twirled impudently, the hall light gleaming on the smooth skin of her shoulders, the rich chestnut of her hair luxuriant, her breasts tight and full against the abrasive material.

Taking the short jacket from her, he helped her put it on. 'There are two schools of thought on that outfit,' he murmured near to her ear, blue eyes smoky as she turned to face him. 'One which I'll probably share with every man at the restaurant tonight.'

'Oh, yes?' She pretended innocence.

'It revolves very basically around what you're not wearing underneath.' Stroking a wisp of hair behind her ear, he trapped her gaze. 'The second is even more basic.'

'I think I'll pass on that one.' She tore her gaze away as Ted and Kitty came into the hallway to see them off.

While Silas told them where they were going and what time they'd be back Rachael sneaked an appreciative glance at Silas, whose casual dress consisted of a grey suit and black wool shirt. Black, she had to admit, did wonders for him; it drew immediate attention to his hair and shadowed jaw. Female fantasies were made of stuff like this, she admitted, trying to ignore the proprietorial hand resting on her shoulder.

They were going to a restaurant that specialised in traditional Cornish food, called Figgy Hobbin. Rachael had been intrigued by the name, thinking it must hark back to a local character or legend she had failed to come across, only to find that it was a pastry with currants in it. 'Romantic little soul, aren't you?' Silas had been amused by her disappointment and she had avoided his gaze, knowing that his idea of romance was of a much more basic variety.

'You don't need to go to Figgy Hobbin for real Cornish food,' Ted grumbled. 'The owner's a Londoner, you know.'

Silas produced one of his rakish smiles that hinted at ulterior motives without need for words. 'I'm going to show Rachael off. I have to make amends for disappearing for the first week of our honeymoon.'

'It's nice to go out,' Kitty agreed, seeming delighted by Rachael's embarrassed demeanour.

All Rachael could think of was that the dress had

been a mistake! She had worn it in defiance; Silas appeared to have got the wrong message. The word 'honeymoon' had been chosen deliberately to unnerve her and had succeeded. She marched crossly to the car, Silas's soft laughter making her fume as he slid into the driving seat beside her.

'I'm sorry, Rachael,' he apologised with so little sincerity that she merely crossed her arms and stared in frozen silence out of the side window. 'Don't worry. I know an excellent remedy for the way you're feeling.' His hand slid over her knee and he avoided the slap directed at his head. 'Easy, Red——' A smile played around his mouth, widening at her quick, furious glance in his direction. 'A desperate case, I'd say. I'll play doctor later.'

'You'll need one yourself, if you're not careful.' Rachael's emotions were in turmoil. She knew she was handling the situation badly. If anything, Silas responded to her vulnerability, not the spitting virago he had on his hands at the moment. That would be a challenge.

Silas turned the key in the ignition, and with a slight wave of his hand towards the house he turned on to the gravelled road towards the glimmering heathland.

'Whatever happened to the girl who threw all those tantrums over my attitude to women? Then there's the presents you've thrown back at me and the little lectures about burning both ends of the candle.'

'We've already established the fact that I. . .found you attractive,' she reminded him grimly, wishing she hadn't been so horribly transparent.

'Found?'

'All right, find you attractive.' There was no point in denying it; that would only leave her open to his particularly wounding brand of humour.

'Thank you.' His gratitude had as much weight as his

earlier apology and provoked Rachael into a storm of words.

'All right, I admit it. I think you're the most sexually attractive man I've ever met! But I've still got a brain in my head. I'm not nineteen any more. I know you! I've seen you chase women as if they're the only females left on the planet just to drop them with equal speed. What did you expect me to do? Collapse at your feet just because you've decided to notice I'm a woman?'

'I've always been certain of your gender.' He slowed the car to take a difficult bend, the luminous green display on the dashboard shadowing the hollows under his cheekbones. 'I didn't want to hurt you, Rachael. Still don't, for what it's worth.'

'It's inevitable, wouldn't you say?' She huddled back into her seat. 'Why do we have to have this sort of conversation before dinner? We used to be able to spend time together without arguing all the time.'

Silas shook his head and sighed. 'I think it would be better to talk this out. But if you insist on playing the ostrich. . .' His shrug was almost offensive in its negligence. He had cut the ground from under Scott's feet in a similar manner earlier that day and she was quick to recognise the tactic.

'Fine.' She schooled her temper with an effort. 'Tell me about Figgy Hobbin. Do you eat there regularly when you're at home? Is it very olde worlde?'

'You'll see for yourself soon,' he returned smoothly. 'I've been there once or twice before. I don't usually socialise much when I'm at Winterbrook. I don't have much time to spend here, so when I do get the odd week off I just relax, visit friends and take Ted off to the local. Very dull for a jet-setter, I'm afraid; I trust you'll keep my secret.'

Rachael swallowed; taking a deep breath, she muttered, 'Sorry.' Game, set and match to Silas. He had neatly pointed out that she was back in the old groove, judging him from the superficial relationship shared by a secretary and employer. He wanted to talk and resolve the gulf between them and increasingly had to rely on provoking her temper as the only means of communication.

He didn't acknowledge her apology, his attention diverted by the task of parking the car. Rachael hardly noticed their surroundings. Figgy Hobbin was in St Agnes, over twenty miles away from Winterbrook, and the small coastal village immediately appealed to Rachael's idea of what Cornwall should be like. She forgot her quarrel with Silas and pushed open the passenger door, breathing in the raw sea air.

The restaurant was a long, low building, dimly lit with the incongruous addition of an old fishing boat lying on cobbles and reeking of oil and fish. It was straight out of Daphne du Maurier, with a knowing wink to the customer that invited them to join in the pretence.

'I don't think we've ever been anywhere so nice.' She smiled up at Silas when he came around the car to join her.

His look was totally derisive. 'That sort of remark would make most of the world's restaurateurs suicidal. Are you totally unimpressed by all that glamour I've thrown at you over the years? I always thought you enjoyed our holidays together.'

'They weren't holidays. I had to work, remember.' Rachael eyed him nervously as he narrowed the distance between them, her back coming into contact with the metal body of the car.

'Kiss me.' It was a challenge, one that nearly made Rachael march swiftly past him to the restaurant. But the knowledge, that, however hard she struggled, it was self-defeating, stopped her. She found his sudden interest intoxicating and denying it wasn't fooling either of them.

'What, in public?' Her outrage sounded rather diffident. She swallowed drily as he slid his hands inside her jacket to rest lightly against her waist.

'It's not exactly overcrowded.' Moodily he surveyed her troubled features, his dark hair riffled by the wind. 'You're not a coward, Rachael.' His hold tightened. 'Fight for what you want.'

What did she want? Silas madly in love with her? She tried to deny the dream but it haunted her day and night. Lifting vulnerable dark eyes to the search of his, she reached up for him, her body curving in to his as he urged her closer. Soft lips met the firm demand of Silas's mouth, her fingers sliding around his neck into the thick black hair that fringed his collar. The wild clamour in her body was indecent. Her mouth opened in welcome submission, her tongue touching his in a hot, fiery dance that forgot time, place, everything. The metal of the car was cold against her thighs as she felt the weight of Silas lower body, telling her more clearly than words that he wanted her, and wanted her badly! Gasping for breath, her mouth felt cold when he released it and pushed her hair back from her throat before biting softly at the creamy skin revealed. The night sky swung back into view, the thin sliver of the moon bright and hard in the sky. A car passed them, intending to park.

Silas drew back with obvious reluctance. Leaning against the roof of the car and taking her hand in his, he pressed it against his heart. The violent beat made her seek his eyes.

'Frightening, isn't it?' His voice had a rough edge to it. 'Let's go and eat dinner before I change my mind.'

Rachael's mind was in a whirl. She had suspected that Silas's touch would have a devastating effect on her, but never in her wildest dreams had she imagined she would affect him the same way.

Rachael was seated at the table, given a menu in a dream state. It was only when she was asked if she wanted an aperitif that she broke out of the spell and took in her surroundings. The restaurant was designed to look like the lower deck of a boat. Pewter mugs and serving utensils decorated the walls, a great cauldron filled with jutting wine bottles served as a wine bar and barrels stacked one on top of the other continued the fantasy.

'It's wonderful.' Her childlike delight was met with an indulgent smile that made her toes curl.

'I'm glad you like it.' He tasted the wine, nodding his approval to the waiter, sitting back in his chair, consulting the menu. 'I suggest the crab soup, followed by squab pie and burnt cream pudding.'

She agreed, quite happy for him to order while she questioned him on some of the more obscure dishes. He corrected her pronunciation, amused by her curiosity, a warmth in his eyes that was quite different from the way he usually looked at her.

The squab pie was a combination of lamb and pigeon breasts, cooked with apple and onions. It was delicious and she ate with a surprisingly good appetite. They talked easily, Silas impressed by the knowledge she had gained about the area in her short time in Cornwall. It was a golden opportunity to bring up the question of how long they were to spend in England. Silas seemed perfectly willing to discuss the subject.

'When I first decided to take full responsibility for Tristan, I envisaged moving Tredegar and Pitt's centre of operations to London,' he admitted. 'I had a home, a son.' He narrowed his eyes in a mock scowl. 'I naïvely thought a wife would fit neatly into the package.'

'You meant to make Winterbrook your home?' She

clarified the point, a troubled frown marring her brow
at his nod of agreement. 'And you would presumably
spend the week in London and come home at the
weekend. Business trips included, that doesn't sound
like much of a commitment, Silas.'

'No.' His smile was charm itself. 'But then I saw
myself as something of a martyr. I was presented with
a situation that wasn't of my choosing. I didn't know
Tris all that well, my business trip to England was
about that——'

'But you nearly blew a fuse when I wouldn't come
with you,' she interrupted, the realisation dawning that
she had been included in his plans before he discovered
Michael's debts.

'Hmm.' He regarded her speculatively. 'Two things
occurred to me simultaneously. One, that if I got
married you'd leave me, and secondly if you took the
plunge you'd presumably do the same thing. I suppose
I had it in mind then that you'd fit in rather well with
the scheme of things. I took you for granted; I'm
sorry.' He leant back in his chair, saluting her with his
glass. 'You gave me a shock when you refused to come
to England with me; it put things into a different
perspective.'

'In other words, blackmail,' she challenged him, but
he refused to be ruffled, a silent message conveyed by
those wicked blue eyes.

'Blackmail,' he repeated the word but there was an
inflexion in his voice that stopped short of agreement.
For some reason she blushed and didn't pursue the
point. That particular path led to a minefield and a
healthy desire for self-preservation made her change
the subject back to their earlier discussion.

'I'd like to spend part of the year at Winterbrook,'
Silas admitted when she pressed him on the point. 'At
the moment there's the project in Exeter that should

keep us here until Christmas. Winterbrook needs reno-
vating; I've had plans drawn up for structural alterations. If you want to change anything you can consult
the architects. The rest is up to you. Just as long as you
keep the spirit of the house in mind, you can have a
free hand.'

And pigs might fly, Rachael thought, a smile pulling
at the corners of her mouth. Silas loved the old barn
and she guessed that he had a clear mental picture of
the modernised Winterbrook that would clash with any
interpretation she might make. Her role, if she guessed
accurately, would be that of a glorified foreman,
making sure schedules were met and plans were kept
to.

'Why are you smiling?' Silas put down his glass and
reached out for her hand. 'Did I say anything amusing
or does your imagination fail you when it comes to
Winterbrook? Is it really that bad?' he demanded, half
laughing. 'I know Mandy shivers at the very mention
of the house, but she doesn't have your robust good
health. I thought you might find it a challenge.'

'Oh, I do, I do,' Rachael chuckled. 'I seem to have
taken on quite a few challenges lately. Married life
certainly isn't dull.'

She knew as soon as she spoke that she had left
herself wide open for one of her husband's provoking
remarks, but he merely held her gaze before lowering
his eyes to study the betraying quiver of her lips.

'Shall we go?' he asked softly, raising an interroga-
tive eyebrow at her startled expression. 'It's nearly
twelve.'

Rachael was genuinely surprised. The evening had
passed so quickly! 'Yes, of course. You must be tired.'
She rose to her feet, managing to avoid looking at him
as she collected her handbag. Sleep, she guessed, was
the last thing on his mind, and a tingle of fevered
anticipation swept over her, making her shiver.

'Cold?' Silas asked solicitously.

She gave an inarticulate murmur in reply, the chill wind outside the restaurant making hardly any impression against her heated flesh.

'Here.' He gave her a car rug once inside the car, switching on the heater and then turning away to fasten his seatbelt and starting up the ignition.

A cassette of the easy listening variety took away any great need for conversation and Rachael falsely assumed that she had regained her composure until Winterbrook came into sight. She was seized by a feeling of unutterable panic. As soon as they were out of the car and in the hallway she made an excuse about looking in on Tristan and hurried up the stairs, aware that Silas watched her flight, hearing the clink of car keys as he tossed them in the air and caught them with a quick snatch of his hand that spoke volumes.

Tristan was sleeping soundly, one arm flung above his head, revealing the clown pattern on his pyjama sleeve. She let her fingers stroke over his silky black hair, her panic receding for a moment as his mouth curled into a smile and he nuzzled the sheet before becoming still again. Tristan was the one uncomplicated part of the deal, she reflected, wishing contrarily that she hadn't bolted from Silas. Escape was fleeting; she couldn't leave the house even if she wanted to, not with Michael's gambling debts on her conscience. Silas had been patient with her, giving her such assurances of permanence as he could. She couldn't demand that he loved her. It was dishonest to keep throwing his past back at him. He had never attempted to treat her badly; in fact, she could remember times when he had defended her from over-amorous business associates whose track record bore a marked similarity to his own.

Rachael tensed as she heard movements in the adjoining bedroom. It was the hardest thing she had ever had to do, walking the short distance to the master bedroom. Taking a deep breath, she opened the door.

'Tristan's all right, I trust.' Silas took off his jacket; his voice had icicles in it and his regard wasn't much warmer.

'It's my job to make sure he is, isn't it?' she asked haughtily, his tone putting her immediately on the defensive.

'I don't think we ought to discuss job descriptions, do you?' His shadow played over the walls and ceiling. The main light wasn't on, just the wall lights. The fire drew her and she went towards it, aware that Silas had begun to unbutton his shirt.

'I'm nervous, Silas.' She splayed her hands out to be heated by the flames. 'There's no need for you to take it as a personal insult.'

The silence stretched out interminably. Rachael moved restlessly as she felt him approach, trembling as his hands smoothed over her shoulders and down her arms comfortingly.

'I'm only human, Rachael.' His breath warmed the side of her face as he traced her hairline with his lips. 'You wear that dress, kiss me as if you can't wait and then turn back into Rachael the secretary. I'm very fond of Rachael the secretary.' He tried to lighten the atmosphere. 'But I want the woman.'

Fond—the word lashed at her; such a tame emotion compared to what she was feeling. She felt the coolness of air on her neck as Silas gathered up the weight of her hair in his hands and let it silk through his fingers.

'While you were scribbling your shorthand. . .' his voice was distracted and husky '. . . I had some hot fantasies about undressing you.'

She shuddered, feeling him recapture her hair. 'You don't have to say things like that, Silas. I know I'm nothing like your usual type. . .' Not the Paris type, she thought, unable to turn and see the compassion that would greet her words.

'We stayed so long in Malaysia because I was addicted to watching you in the pool. You're a very sexy lady.' He turned her to face him. 'It's natural with you, there's no artifice involved.'

'Silas!' His voice was weaving a heady magic and yet she couldn't believe he felt such things about her.

He ignored her. 'The second school of thought about this dress,' he continued their earlier conversation, 'is how quickly it can be taken off.' Easing the denim jacket over her shoulder, his dark head bent and she swallowed thickly as his mouth fused hotly against skin and underlying bone. His black hair tickled her cheek and she turned her face into the clean, vital warmth, feeling the muscles shift in his chest and arms as he brought her against him. She wasn't allowed to hide for long; raising his head, Silas separated her other shoulder from the dark material, his fingers sliding under the jacket and urging it down her arms. It fell to the floor and she moved to pick it up but was caught against him.

'Take off my shirt.' It was already open and the brown skin tantalised her unbearably. Fine black hair was scattered in a rough cross on his chest.

It wasn't fair that one man should have so much; Rachael's mind was clouded by her task. Her heart hammered against her breastbone; she was aware of the heat in the blue gaze watching her movements. When his shirt joined her jacket, he let his arms close around her shoulders so that her face was pressed against his chest and she was breathing in the scent from his skin, his body hair teasing her lips. Silas was as tense as she had ever known him.

'God, if you knew how much I wanted you to touch me, you'd take pity on me. Hell, Rachael, some of it must come naturally——' He broke off as she nipped him with her teeth. The heartfelt groan against Rachael's ear seemed to ignite something deep within her. Her hands began to roam over his skin, her face lifting to his, her mouth devoured hungrily as Silas demonstrated what frustration could do to a man. His tongue very explicitly told her what he wanted, her head falling back over his arm as his mouth dragged free and his teeth nibbled at her chin before sliding moistly down her throat to the small bones at the base of her throat. His other hand hooked behind her knee, drawing it up against his hip, his fingers deftly freeing her stocking from her suspender belt and chasing the silk down to her slim ankle, easing both stocking and shoe from her foot.

Silas was used to undressing women. Bare-legged and with only her dress and the silk guarding her loins left to clothe her, Rachael found herself reluctant to offer any resistance as the black denim dress was drawn down her arms and she felt the scrape of denim over the sensitive tip of her nipple.

'I should have taken you earlier.' Silas let his fingers slide down the slope of her breast, his lips a bare inch from hers. 'It's been torture, hasn't it?'

Yes, it had, but it was only now that she was beginning to appreciate just how much control she had exerted over herself.

'You need to be stroked.' His voice wound erotically around every protest bubbling in her mind and cocooned them in a sea of sensuality. 'You're aching for me.' His finger teasingly circled one tight nipple. 'I ache too.'

'Oh, God!' She clutched at his hair as his mouth followed the path of his finger and felt the warmth and tormenting cold as he let the rosy crest slip from between his lips and then captured it again.

Silas raised his head, taking in the heated colour running along her cheekbones, the tense excitement evident in the glitter of her eyes and the trembling softness of her lips. Tracing her mouth with his fingers, he stroked her throat, the hollow wells of her collar-bone, brushing lightly over the swell of her breasts and finding the stiff denim resting over her hips.

'Just me?' he questioned softly, as the tug of the material down over her thighs dislodged her silk panties.

Aware of his curiosity with regard to her level of experience, she realised she was incredibly naïve compared to other women of her age. Guessing her answer, he kissed her tenderly.

'Try to relax.' His palm flattened against her stomach. Rachael took a deep shaken breath, moving restlessly as he brushed gently over the shadow of hair protecting her femininity.

'It's good, I promise,' he responded to the dazed question in her eyes, watching them close as he gave in to the overwhelming demands of his masculine nature and touched her with increasing intimacy. If Rachael had imagined her initiation into the realms of sensuality would be fraught with awkwardness and embarrass-ment, nothing could have been further from the truth. Silas made it beautiful for her. It was dreadful as well because it left her totally vulnerable to him.

His touch turned her legs to jelly and she was grateful for the strong arm, sweeping them from under her, and lifting her on to the bed. Silas divested himself of his remaining clothes and came back to her, pulling her back into his arms as if he was afraid she would leave. Urgency swept them quickly into a maelstrom of passion. His warmth was alien, so too the hardness of muscle and bone bearing down on her.

'Easy, Red.' Concern fought with the primitive need for conquest when he felt her body stiffen, her untried womanhood giving way to the demand of his body.

'Cry it out.' He kissed her eyelids as they fluttered closed.

'Ah!' His back arched as her nails dug into him but the choked cry she gave made him watch her between narrowed lids. Stroking the damp hair from her forehead, his jaw was tight with restraint. His control was going. When her lashes parted, he drowned in the heat in her eyes. Kissing her, Silas meant to be gentle, but it got out of hand.

Rachael twisted restlessly beneath him, her legs entangling with his, feeling the rough hair against her slim calves, the surging strength of his body sending shock waves through her. They entwined, like a living sculpture, the pure male beauty which Silas possessed covering the soft, living warmth of the woman beneath him, her pale thighs spread to cradle him. When she cried out a second time, it was a sound of a woman driven to complete fulfilment. Silas shuddered against her, groaning into her ear as he subsided against her in hot, sweat-slicked exhaustion.

Rachael stared unseeing into the darkness, her body languid, embers of heat still sparking, not allowing her to drift into sleep. Silas had taken his weight from her and she turned her head to find him looking at her.

'Still feel nervous?' His voice was like rough velvet, his gaze admiring as it swept over her abandoned nakedness. She merely returned his stare. Slowly, he reached for her. She let him pull her down on top of him, her hair spreading around them in a curtain as her mouth sought the warmth of his with all the fervour of an addict.

CHAPTER FIVE

RACHAEL looked out to sea. She had risen before Silas that morning, leaving the room without waking him, taking the car keys and creeping out of the house before anyone could discover her. She hadn't a clue where she was. The wind-blasted, stormy West of England had, as Scott predicted, become an oasis of sun and blue skies. The rocky bay which she had discovered was quite beautiful, full of golden sand, sun glittering on surf and the joyous squawk of seagulls. She watched the gulls for a moment, seeing one climb high on a thermal current and glide, surveying all below. She felt a stab of envy. Flying away seemed like a very good idea.

It had never occurred to Rachael that she was in danger of loving Silas more than she had done in the last three years. She hadn't thought it possible! Of course, she had never called it love. Infatuation, something that had to be strictly controlled, had been the label she had put upon it. But now it was time to face the truth. If only she had admitted the strength of her feelings before, common sense would have dictated that she get as far away from Silas as possible. Now that Silas was no longer an unattainable fantasy man, the usual course of events with such obsessions was for interest to wane. Instead, she had discovered a Silas who was infinitely more complex than the work-hard, play-hard businessman she was accustomed to.

Walking across the sands, she paused to take off her shoes and let her bare toes come into contact with the small pools left by the receding tide. It was cold at first but her skin soon adjusted to the temperature. Picking up a handful of pebbles, she threw them, one by one, into the sea, watching the splash they made with indifference. Had she changed for him? He had said that they both had a great deal to learn about each other but she suspected that she was the one in the dark. Ever since the night in his Manhattan apartment, when he had put the question of marriage to her, he had been confident of her agreement. Michael's debts had allowed her to save face; when it came to it, she doubted that she would have had the strength to leave his employment, and had he been married to someone else the situation would have been unbearable.

'Oh, God, if he knows. . .' She left the sentence unfinished, throwing the remaining pebbles into the sea in a scatter. She hardly monitored the ensuing explosion of water, her mind slipping back to the night before. Memories of her body curling into his, warm limbs entangled, and the touch of his fingers as he traced her cheekbones. He had tilted her chin to look down into her face, his breathing still erratic from the passion they had shared, and his gaze had been like a searchlight into her soul.

'What do you want? What do you want, damn you!' she whispered into the wind, responding to the question in his eyes as if she was still in Winterbrook, still in his arms. Did he want her to love him? Silly question, really; he depended upon her devotion, not for himself but for Tristan's security. Did he care for the child so much that he was willing to sacrifice Rachael's happiness as well as his own, or did it go beyond Tristan to the shadowy figure of Amanda Tredegar? Silas and Scott were antagonists; she could be wrong, but when Silas had told her that revealing Tristan's parentage would hurt someone he cared a great deal for she didn't think he was talking about his cousin.

Rachael removed the lime-green jersey-style jacket

she had pulled on, wary, despite the promise of the morning, and let the sun's heat warm her skin. Underneath, she wore an all-in-one combination of sun-top and trousers, the white cotton patterned with small multicoloured motifs, a dark green belt with silver buckle slung low on her waist. With her mass of auburn hair tied back she looked like a teenager. She felt a million miles away from Iowa and small town dances. She remembered the desperation of the 'right' dress and the success of the evening being dependent on Billy Laselle's smile. He had gone on to sell farm machinery, she recalled; had grown a moustache that made him look like a weasel and had a reputation with the ladies. She suspected she had a weakness for rogues.

What was she going to do? What *could* she do? She was the slave to a fascination that she had lived with for three years; what was so different now? But it was different. She had Silas's promise of fidelity and she believed he was sincere. He cared for her in his own way; he would do his best not to hurt her. But his love—if that was pledged elsewhere in a hopeless yearning for his cousin's wife, could she cope with knowing that she was merely a substitute?

Unable to come to any firm resolution, she made her way back to the parked car. She was going to have to hire another car for herself, otherwise she would be trapped in Winterbrook when Silas was out on business. Glancing at her watch, she was surprised to see that it was after nine and, quickly unlocking the car door, she began the journey back to the house.

The nagging suspicion that Silas had a meeting with an architect he was planning to use for the renovation of Winterbrook that morning made her drive more speedily that usual. It wasn't until a car swerved past her, blaring its horn, that she realised she was on the wrong side of the road, and took the rest of the journey with greater caution.

Parking the car in the courtyard, she wasn't totally surprised to see Silas stride out of the house and wrench open her door.

'Where the hell have you been?' He unfastened her seatbelt before she could gather her wits and dragged her out of the car. Dressed in a dark blue business suit, he had regained his customary elegance but the sheer fury in his eyes made him look anything but the cool, assured professional.

'Have I made you late?' she began apologetically, wincing as he slammed the door shut and turned on her.

'Late,' he said so quietly that it made her jump. 'Oh, yes, of course, you know how I hate missing appointments.' The sarcasm was vitriolic.

'I didn't mean to keep the car so long. . .' She attempted to placate him as he hauled her to the house.

'I wasn't aware I'd given you permission to drive it,' he said between gritted teeth. 'I have rather nightmarish memories of your attempting to go the wrong way around Piccadilly Circus on one of our previous trips.'

'I did not!' she defended herself indignantly. 'Besides, I need a car and I meant to be back before nine. I didn't know I needed permission to drive your car. What am I supposed to do? Ring for a taxi every time I want to go out?'

'You could have asked me. This morning I would have driven you anywhere you cared to go.' His eyes blazed into hers, meeting an equal amount of fire. 'Anywhere.' He reinforced the statement with a hard kiss upon Rachael's surprised mouth.

She didn't get the chance to reply. Kitty came out of the kitchen and smiled with relief when she saw Rachael.

'You've come back, then.' Glancing at Silas, the

older woman caught her lip with her teeth, accurately gauging his mood. 'Would you like some coffee?'

'Yes, that's very kind of you.' Rachael finished the sentence over her shoulder as Silas marched her towards the study, impervious to Kitty's curiosity.

'I don't know what Kitty thought,' she gulped, backing into the room as he closed the door with unnecessary firmness, glaring at her, blue eyes livid.

'I should imagine she thinks we've had a row. Tell me, is this something I'm going to have to get used to, these little disappearing acts first thing in the morning? Or perhaps it was some kind of primeval celebration of womanhood, a need to feel at one with nature.'

She felt hurt by his gibes, even though she could tell her disappearance had upset him. He was right in a way. She had disliked his 'Rachael the secretary' digs but that was what she had been: becoming his wife was not just sharing his bed; there were certain mental adjustments to make as well.

'I just needed a little time to myself. I'm sorry if you were worried.'

'Worried,' he repeated with force. 'You drive like a lunatic at the best of times; I didn't know what frame of mind you'd be in this morning. I've spent the worst two hours of my life and you give me a trite little apology about needing time to yourself.' He crossed the room to join her near the fireplace and received a hostile glance as the aggressive line of his body threatened hers.

'My driving is quite adequate, thank you.' She tried to forget the near-brush on the moor road, knowing that her skill behind the wheel wasn't the real bone of contention. As she pushed a hand through her wind-blown hair, her dark eyes were defensive. 'I repeat, I'm sorry if you were worried; next time I'll remember to ask permission. Is that all right, sir?'

She received the impression that if she had been a

man he would have greeted the uplift of her jaw with a right hook that would have knocked her head off her shoulders. As it was, he grabbed the front of her outfit and hauled her up against him.

'I have a very bad temper, Rachael.' His mouth was stiff as he spoke. 'Don't push your luck.'

She subsided a little, noting the shifting muscle in his jaw and acknowledging that she couldn't remember seeing him in such a state before. Her earlier belligerence was replaced by an appreciation of his concern that made her eyes soften. Maybe it had been a little thoughtless to disappear like that. She should have left a note. The tension uncoiled slowly between them and Silas released his grip on her clothing and brought her to rest against his chest.

'When I first made love to a girl,' he confided, with a degree of self-mockery, 'I felt on top of the world. Not because the first time was one of life's ultimate experiences; it was something to do with gaining membership into adult manhood, being one of the boys. With women, I guess, it's a little different.'

She knew he was trying to give her an opening to express herself on the subject but it was impossible for her to share the jumble of feelings evoked by the previous night in his arms.

'A little different,' she agreed, keeping the conversation superficial.

Silas's eyes darkened. 'You're not one of the world's greatest communicators, are you? You went up in flames last night; why are you so frosty this morning?'

'I'm not,' she denied his accusation, her eyes wide and honest. She realised her reticence provoked him but it was something she couldn't help.

'I give up.' He regarded her with exasperation. 'I've got to go. I've had to put Anderson off twice already.' Bending his dark head, he kissed her. Their lips clung, the kiss the one they should have shared that morning.

Why hadn't she stayed in bed? Once such wanton thoughts would have shocked her, but her reactions to his closeness numbed all sense of propriety. The regret in his eyes soothed her somewhat. 'We have an engagement for dinner tonight. I'm sorry.' He smoothed a brief kiss over her eyebrow. 'I thought a few social engagements might ease the tension between us. As it turns out, I'd like to cancel, but Mandy does take her time preparing these things and she doesn't get out much.'

Her disappointment at finding she would have to share Silas deepened considerably when she found out who with. She could live in cloud-cuckoo-land while Amanda Tredegar remained in the shadows but the prospective meeting fuelled the uncertainty that was characteristic of her feelings towards their marriage.

'You'll like her,' he promised. A quick glance at his watch showed him that he was late and he released her as Kitty entered the room with the coffee-tray.

'Mr Anderson had called again, Silas,' Kitty informed him. 'He asked if you would let him know if you couldn't see him this morning.'

'I'm on my way. I'll see about a car for you, Rachael.' He spoke over his shoulder, lifting his hand in a goodbye salute as he left the room.

Tristan occupied most of her day. When she wasn't playing with him, he would follow at her heels. She laughed at him when he duplicated her absent-minded ramble around the furniture in the parlour. She had been mulling over the idea of spending most of the year in England and hadn't been aware of the miniature mimic. He laughed because she laughed but looked puzzled at the same time. A minute later he tripped over the rug and she saw his little dark head lift, his bottom lip wobbling as he waited for her response. She picked him up, knowing a big fuss would convince him he was badly hurt, when it was really more shock than anything else. Holding him close, she selected a story-book and sat with him on her knee.

'That one.' He pointed at a picture of an elephant dressed in a ringmaster's outfit.

'Oh, the one about the el-e-phant.' She stressed each syllable, knowing that 'nellybunt' was as near as he got to the pronunciation.

'He's happy with you,' Kitty commented, coming in to ask when she wanted tea. 'Poor little love, it's a good thing Silas has got a sense of responsibility; that Scott——'

'Scott loves him.' Rachael spoke with such certainty it made the older woman stare at her in surprise. 'It would be hard not to,' she hurried on, realising it might sound impertinent to speak with such authority after such a short time at Winterbrook.

Kitty smiled, chucking Tristan under his chin and earning a big smile in return. 'That's true enough. It's his poor mother I feel sorry for. She should have known better than get mixed up with a married man, but she was young. . .' She swallowed and Rachael felt a lump in her own throat. 'She loved Tristan, too.'

Not enough. Rachael cuddled the little boy against her, stricken by the thought. Whatever Mary Deal's feelings for her son, they hadn't been strong enough to build her life around him. It made her shiver, because that was what she was being asked to do, and Tristan wasn't her child. She kissed his forehead and his chubby arms closed around her neck. Something would have to be done, but at the moment she was unable to decide what.

When Silas returned that evening, Rachael had just finished bathing and was putting the finishing touches to her hair with a heated brush. He threw his car keys down on the bedside cabinet, stripping off his jacket and flinging it carelessly on the bed before moving to the bathroom and turning on the taps to refill the bath.

Good evening, Silas, she mouthed to herself in the mirror, watching him reappear. He tugged at his cuff, giving her a long glance before crossing to her side and offering her his wrist, the mangled linen showing that he had made a considerable effort before asking her assistance.

'I was flagged down on the way home.' He let her undo the second cufflink, his tone level but holding a dangerous undercurrent. 'By a man who seemed to think I'd driven straight for him this morning. You weren't driving on the wrong side of the road, were you, Rachael?' he asked silkily. 'Or do you think my— er—neurosis where your driving is concerned is so strong that I'm starting to influence other people?'

She raised her head as the second cufflink came free, her face holding the innocence of an angel. 'I suppose he could have mistaken the car.' She tried to stifle the memories of the night before but saw an answering awareness in his gaze as it roved over her face.

'It's possible.' He didn't sound convinced, but some of the menace drained from his voice. 'I spoke to someone at the local employment agency about hiring a chauffeur. . . Don't argue, Rachael.' He bent and kissed her forehead. 'With all the alterations being done to the house, Ted will be grateful to have a younger man around. It will leave you free to keep an eye on Tristan. He already knows how to undo a seatbelt; he's not safe in the back by himself.'

All perfectly reasonable, she summarised resentfully. A chauffeur, of course, had another advantage; she couldn't disappear in the early morning and Silas had a watchdog permanently on patrol.

'I want you safe.' Silas moved into the personal arena, his voice husky and compulsive. 'I don't want what goes on between us putting you in danger.'

Take 4 Medical Romances

Mills & Boon Medical Romances capture all the excitement and emotion of a busy medical world... A world, however, where love and romance are never far away.

We will send you 4 MEDICAL ROMANCES absolutely FREE plus a cuddly teddy bear and a mystery gift, as your introduction to this superb series.

At the same time we'll reserve a subscription for you to our Reader Service.

Every month you could receive the 4 latest Medical Romances delivered direct to your door postage and packing FREE, plus a free Newsletter filled with competitions, author news and much more.

And remember there's no obligation, you may cancel or suspend your subscription at any time. So you've nothing to lose and a world of romance to gain!

FREE

Your Free Gifts!

Return this card, and we'll send you a lovely little soft brown bear together with a mystery gift... So don't delay!

Rachael let him draw her up into his arms without a murmur. She was so totally wrapped up in his spell that when he bit her ear reprovingly she raised her lashes, wanting him and letting it show.

'I'll have to go to the bath or it will come to me.' He spoke lightly, one thumb brushing over the sensuous curves of her mouth. 'Want to scrub my back?' A smile touched his mouth as she drew back, embarrassed, muttering something about getting changed.

Driving along the narrow country lanes between Winterbrook and Scott's house, Thornfield, an hour later, Rachael's hard-won calm was barely threatened. Apart from commenting favourably on the outfit she had chosen, Silas spoke little. She had decided on the white two-piece largely because it was cool and elegant at the same time. The storm-force winds which she had become to think were a permanent climatic feature had exhausted themselves and there was hardly a breath of wind to be had.

Aware that her brazen outfit the evening before had been interpreted as a fairly blatant invitation, she had tried to be a little more demure. Her outfit combined a voluminous white top, caught in with a silver wrought belt to emphasise her narrow waistline, and a graceful calf-length skirt. Delicate white sandals had been added as a token rebellion to the heathland that made wellington boots or walking shoes more practical.

'Thornfield,' she mused lightly, more to break the oppressive silence than any real interest in the question she asked. 'Thornfield and Winterbrook. They're not exactly cosy names to live with, are they? Did your ancestors prefer the savage to the more usual Manor House or Gables?'

'I dare say there is a flair for drama in the family but the names were taken from the land. Thornfield was probably built on a bramble patch.' He smiled at her chuckle of amusement, a hint of warmth momentarily relieving the serious expression he had worn for most of the journey.

'I concede Thornfield.' She watched him as he drove, wondering why a visit to his cousin's home should make him so sombre. 'But Winterbrook. It could have been Springbrook or Summerbrook. No,' she argued with herself. 'I think it was a comment on the lack of heating.'

Silas laughed. 'Actually, it's named Winterbrook because the brook swells with the winter rains. I promise you central heating for the winter. I don't want you getting cold.' The smile lingering around his mouth made her blush but he was too busy concentrating on the winding road to notice.

A prickle of tension crawled along Rachael's spine as they neared Thornfield House. Scott's home was brightly lit and welcoming but her early forebodings about Amanda Tredegar and her importance in Silas's life made it impossible for Rachael to fully relax.

'Glad you could make it,' Scott drawled in greeting, his dark blue velvet jacket comfortably shabby compared to the immaculate lines of Silas's traditional black. 'You two look as if you've just stepped out of *Vogue*.' He ran an appreciative eye over Rachael's slender figure, admiring the Iowa tan against the white material that clothed her. 'You'll embarrass us poor country folk.'

'Let's call a truce this evening, shall we?' Silas suggested equably. 'We don't want to upset Mandy.' He continued on past Scott as if he were dismissing a rather truculent butler and led Rachael towards one of the larger reception-rooms.

Why Mandy shouldn't be upset soon became apparent. Rachael was still smarting from the fact that Silas awarded her no such consideration when the sight of her hostess made her feel immediately contrite. If Scott had suffered from the shadows of the past, Amanda

Tredegar had been worn thin by them. A delicate, almost brittly fragile woman lay on a silk couch, a walking stick within easy reach, her eyes the colour of violets, lighting up when she saw Silas. Silvery blonde hair, cut in a short, elfin style, emphasised the sculpted beauty of the woman's cheekbones and Rachael, remembering Tristan's robust constitution, reflected that the little boy would be something of a handful if introduced to Scott's home.

'Mandy.' Silas kissed the woman's cheek, stopping her from getting to her feet with a calming stroke of his hands over her shoulders. It was done without drawing attention to the woman's infirmity and exposed Rachael to a host of extremely mixed feelings.

'This is my wife, Rachael.' Silas turned to catch the troubled expression in her eyes, aware of her hasty attempt to conceal her emotions.

'Pleased to meet you.' She approached the couch and took the proffered hand, surprised at its coldness.

'I'm like ice,' Amanda Tredegar admitted. 'Scott said you were nice and I shouldn't be nervous of meeting new people. . .' She looked to her husband for support and he came behind the couch, putting a hand on her shoulder. 'I must get out more.' She sounded perplexed with herself and Rachael smiled with genuine warmth.

'I think the weather makes outings a little more appealing. It's like a different world here when the sun shines.'

'I told you you'd be surprised.' Scott recalled their conversation coming back from Tristan's fishing expedition. 'But if we're going to make a native of you you'll have to learn to love the storms. Silas used to be frightened of them when he was a boy; I soon got him out of that.'

Silas gave his cousin a jaundiced look. 'You laughed at me, as I remember.'

'He got his own back.' Amanda joined in, enjoying their reminiscences. 'He mixed frogspawn with the jam and put it in Scott's sandwiches.'

Rachael laughed, sharing a long look with Silas. She could see a childhood of uneasy threesomes. He seemed to expect her to understand. She did, but had little intention of making this particular triangle into a square. This closed society needed a breath of fresh air; there were too many cobwebs.

Thornfield reflected the style and artistic nature of its owners. Dinner was served in the conservatory, an addition to the house of white wrought iron and glass filled with a profusion of palms.

Mussels with saffron provided the first course, which was dish similar to the French *moules marinière* using cider rather than white wine. Pork with apples and sage followed. It appeared that Amanda had heard about their visit to Figgy Hobbin and was not to be outdone. When Rachael asked, she revealed that she had cooked to traditional recipes. 'I cheated for dessert,' she admitted. 'I adore chocolate mousse, don't you?'

Amanda Tredegar was a very pleasant woman. Rachael liked her despite her natural reluctance to form a friendship with the woman she suspected her husband of loving. She was steeped in the thorniness of this problem when Amanda asked her to come to Thornfield for coffee the next day and to bring Tristan with her.

'I've bought some toys for him,' she confided, making a refusal impossible.

Both men looked stunned at this turn of events, despite the fact it was perfectly normal for an 'aunt' to buy toys for her nephew.

'He's a little tearaway; I'm not sure. . .' Silas tried to put Amanda off but she didn't take his protest seriously.

'Goodness, Silas, he's only two. Rachael will be here

to make sure he doesn't demolish the house. Will you come?' she appealed to Rachael, who could hardly refuse.

Scott remained silent. Rachael guessed he would love to have his son running about in Thornfield but it would be a painful pleasure. Something deep inside her rebelled at all this artifice but she kept her feelings under tight restraint.

Silas, she discovered later that night, had no intention of letting the visit take place. When she asked him just how he intended to rebuff the invitation he merely shrugged.

'Tell her he's got a cold. I'll tell her if you like.'

Rachael sighed impatiently. 'And how long is that going to put her off for? A week? Two weeks? Silas, Scott isn't going to keep away and neither will Amanda. She hasn't got any children; she's looking forward to spoiling her nephew.'

'And Scott comes clean and we all live happily ever after. I can read you like a book.' Back at Winterbrook, Silas cast her a brooding glance from his stance at the fireplace. 'It's not that simple.'

'No, I can see you're determined to keep it as complicated as possible,' Rachael retaliated. She met his fierce glare and approached him warily. 'I'm sorry. I didn't mean that; I know you've tried to do your best.'

'Thank you.' His voice was cold. 'What do you want me to do? Tell her? I promised Scott that I wouldn't do that. And if I did decide to break my word what happens if Amanda finds she can't accept the past? I'm sure Scott would find a shoulder to cry on but Amanda's damn near housebound. I have thought this out before, Rachael; I don't get some kind of vicarious pleasure in seeing people miserable.'

Rachael reluctantly conceded the point but remained firm about the visit. It was impracticable to stop

Amanda meeting Tristan. If anything, Silas's reluctance on the point would only make the woman suspicious. If the Tredegars were going to live a lie for years to come, it was time they got comfortable with it.

'It would seem Michael's gambling debts are weighing heavy.' Silas casually curled his fingers around the silver belt and brought her close to him. 'Paying other people's penances isn't a great deal of fun, is it?'

'This has nothing to do with Michael.' Her fingers tingled with his body warmth as they slid over the white linen of his shirt, while she tried to maintain a distance between them.

'Hasn't it?' He glanced from the darkness of her eyes to the fullness of her lips. 'With Tristan gone, you'll be free. That thought hadn't occurred to you, I suppose?'

'No.' She understood him only too well, her eyes bruised by the cruelty of his threat. 'Thank you for giving me an incentive. There's nothing I'd like more than to get away from you.'

He smiled mockingly. 'Really?' One finger traced the neckline of her top. 'You run away. . .' He followed the movement of his finger, catching the material just below her shoulder and drawing it down her arm. Black, silky lashes lifted, sea-blue eyes engulfing her in a wave of fire. 'But you come back, don't you, my darling?'

'I'm not going to agree with you about Amanda and Tristan.' Her voice broke as his mouth brushed her throat, the pulse there beating urgently against his lips.

'Let's agree to disagree, then,' he murmured, his breath tickling her ear before it too became a victim of his sensual technique. 'I think we can both agree that this is the best part of the deal.'

'Silas!' Her outrage was genuine. His hand had slipped underneath the neckline of her top and squeezed her breast with the finesse of a savage.

'All those models I escorted certainly didn't have

your advantages.' The lazy grin inflamed her even more as she grabbed his wrist and freed herself from his touch.

'I would prefer it if you slept in the dressing-room tonight.' She glared at him. 'I don't respond to blackmail of any kind.'

'You can sleep in the dressing-room, if you wish.' Silas released her. 'You might find it rather airless on such a hot night but if dignity demands it. . .' He was laughing at her and Rachael felt she quite hated him.

'I can stand it if you can, buster,' she muttered under her breath.

Silas opened the door and waved her through, his expression anything but repentant. 'After you, my lady.'

CHAPTER SIX

RACHAEL dressed the next morning with the intention of being cool, practical and very much her old self. She chose a pale blue button-through dress with a wide leather belt and white lace-up shoes. Her auburn hair was helplessly ringletted by the wind and salt tang in the air.

'It's a lovely morning,' Kitty greeted her as she came down to the breakfast table.

'Good morning, darling.' Silas rose from his chair, kissed her cheek and smiled to himself as he returned to his paper. The look she gave him had been malevolent.

'Working?' she enquired, taking in his dark blue suit, the pencil-thin maroon thread alleviating the severity of the colour.

'I'm afraid so.' White teeth crunched a piece of toast. He leisurely surveyed her appearance. 'This afternoon I want to go through the plans for the house with you, so keep yourself available.'

'My time is yours to command.' She gave him a sweet smile and he paused mid-bite and raised an eyebrow.

'Really? I can always rearrange my schedule.' It was a tease but after the restless night she had spent in the dressing-room she was in no mood for Silas's humour. Thanking Kitty for the coffee offered, she sipped it, avoiding his attention rather pointedly.

Kitty glanced from one to the other and raised her eyes to the ceiling.

'They're at it again,' she muttered to her husband, who was polishing the silver in the dining-room.

104

'Young love,' he chuckled, taking his mug of tea. 'What are you worrying about, woman?'

She wrapped her arms around her body and shook her head. 'There'll be no peace until Tristan's settled,' she predicted. 'Rachael's an outsider; she won't see the sense of it. Neither do I; Tristan should be with his father.'

'It isn't any of our business,' Ted reminded her. 'Leave it be.'

In the kitchen Silas was getting ready to depart. 'I'll ring Mandy,' he informed her, catching the swift turn of her head. 'See you later.'

The man was insufferable, Rachael fumed. Totally and utterly insufferable. As it turned out, Amanda Tredegar rang just after ten that morning to commiserate with Tristan's supposed condition.

'Poor little boy.' Amanda was all sympathy. 'I'll bring one of the toys to Winterbrook to cheer him up. It will give me a chance to get out.'

Amanda Tredegar was a determined lady, Rachael decided. Tristan had definitely not got a cold and she had to think on her feet.

'Actually, it's just a sniffle,' Rachael scaled it down. 'It's probably an allergy. Silas is inclined to fuss.'

'Oh, I am glad. I'll see you later, then.'

Rachael felt obliged to offer her lunch and she caught Kitty's eye as she replaced the receiver. 'What else could I do?' She felt guilty and it showed. She didn't agree with Silas over the Amanda and Tristan business but she hadn't intended to go against his wishes in the matter. After all, she was a newcomer to the scene; any intervention on her part would only come after serious contemplation of the issue. Despite her colouring, she was more cautious than impetuous by nature.

'Hard to avoid, them living so close.' Kitty's manner was almost approving. 'Mind you, if Mrs Tredegar gets out more, she might hear some of the gossip. There's not many folk who don't know Scott was involved with Mary Deal.'

Rachael was surprised. She had presumed the matter was a subject of the greatest secrecy. Kitty, she gathered, shared her own feelings of unease with the situation.

The sound of clattering feet made her look to the door and Ted entered, with Tristan doing his best to trip the man up.

'Racha.' Tristan seemed to prefer this form of address to Mummy and Rachael felt dubious enough about her role not to correct him. Besides which, Silas had agreed that Tristan should visit his maternal grandparents every Friday and she thought it might hurt them to hear Tristan use the term to another woman. 'I saw a horse.'

'It was a donkey.' Ted chuckled and ruffled the silky black hair.

'Scott's wife's on her way.' Kitty came straight to the point. 'She's invited for lunch.'

Ted looked dubious but made no comment. No one was in any doubt about Silas's reaction. He would not be pleased!

Amanda Tredegar was totally oblivious to the consternation caused by her visit to Winterbrook House. She had been driven the few miles from Thornfield by the gardener and was very pleased with herself. It was hard not to be caught up in her pleasure and Rachael gave in and smiled welcomingly.

They had lunch in the garden, the lawn an oasis of green surrounded by the heather and bracken of the heathland. Rachael had decided on a chicken salad.

The heat was close and oppressive, the land giving up its moisture to the air and making the atmosphere clammy, prophetic of a building storm.

Tristan had a white peaked cap on his head and was liberally covered in sun cream. He came to inspect

Amanda Tredegar, his eyes moving to the walking stick and growing wide.

'This is Tristan.' Rachael introduced the pair. 'This is Amanda, Tristan.' She couldn't say Aunt Amanda; it stuck in her throat. She would make a dreadful liar, she realised, reflecting darkly that such talents had never been in her desired repertoire of skills. Aware of Tristan's continuing fascination with the stick and Amanda's flushed cheeks, she asked if she could borrow it.

Amanda looked surprised but agreed, laughing when Rachael used her scarf to make it into a puppet and gave it Bronx accent. The following show had both Tristan and his new aunt in peals of laughter. The awkwardness over the stick was completely forgotten.

'Did you have younger children to care for in your family?' Amanda asked, intrigued by Rachael's ease with the boy.

'Only my brother. There's just two years between us. It's amazing what you'll resort to when you've got a bored little boy on your hands.'

'Yes.' Amanda was openly curious. 'You seem to have coped very well, Rachael. It can't have been easy——' She broke off, her delicate colouring suffusing with colour. 'I'm sorry, that must have sounded. . .'

'It's all right.' Rachael tried to think of something to say. Amanda, no doubt, thought she was a paragon of virtue overlooking Silas's misdemeanours. 'I—er—knew the score when I married Silas, and Tristan, well. . .' She watched him chasing a butterfly and laughed when it flew past his nose. 'He's very easy to love.'

'Yes.' Amanda was wistful. 'He's certainly a Tredegar. He'll be another heartbreaker when he gets older. He seems a lot better.' She lightened the mood, referring to the illness.

'Yes, I think it was probably a touch of hay fever.' Rachael gratefully followed her cue.

They returned to the house after lunch, the sun too strong for Tristan to stay out for long. Amanda had produced the promised toy and demonstrated to the eager little boy how it worked. It was a battery-operated robot with a host of flashing lights. It was also very noisy. Rachael barely picked up the sound of gravel crunching under the wheels of a car. She stiffened. Now for the fireworks! She experienced a pang of regret over another night spent in silent battle with Silas while the heatwave made anything more than the cover of a sheet over naked skin unbearable.

The robot introduced itself first, followed by a giggling Tristan. Silas crouched down to inspect the new toy, admiring it as the boy exclaimed over it enthusiastically.

'Where did you get that?' Silas enquired, not recognising it, and then he froze hearing the sound of female voices.

'Manda,' Tristan informed him, getting hold of his hand. 'Come on.'

Silas entered the room, his expression unreadable. 'It's a long time since you've been here, Mandy,' he greeted his cousin's wife. 'This is a historic moment; we're about to redecorate.'

She smiled, accepting the kiss he brushed against her cheek. 'About time too. Old George didn't spend a penny on the place. I don't know how Rachael has put up with it, what with all the glamorous places the two of you have visited, I'm surprised you chose Winterbrook for a honeymoon.'

'Rachael has a hardy nature.' He came to sit on the arm of her chair. 'What she can't beat, she changes.'

Perfectly aware of his meaning, Rachael was conscious of his arm, resting above her shoulders, tensing as his fingers entwined in her hair.

Tristan picked up the robot and took it across to the fair woman, showing proudly that he had demobilised it. All it could do was vainly kick its legs.

'Me Tarzan, you robot.' Amanda's laughter tinkled over them.

'Me Tarzan, you in trouble,' Silas breathed into Rachael's ear as Tristan exploited his new source of attention.

'Me innocent,' Rachael replied in an undertone, feeling the grip on her hair tighten slightly before she was released.

By the time Amanda Tredegar left she had made a firm friend of Tristan, who waved enthusiastically out of the window until she was out of sight.

'Heartwarming,' Silas commented without enthusiasm.

'Did you want her to dislike him?' she enquired provocatively.

'It just adds you and Tris to the deception.' Silas regarded her with a hint of exasperation. 'If she finds out about Scott, she'll know just about everyone she cares about has deceived her. How would you feel?'

'I'd prefer to know the truth!' Rachael held doggedly to her point of view, wishing at the same time she could avoid coming to loggerheads over the issue.

'You're a great one for the truth, aren't you, Rachael?' He pushed a hand through his dark hair, looking weary, missing the wounded look she gave him. 'I suppose the answer would be to move elsewhere, but then there's Tristan's grandparents. He's all they've got left of Mary.'

'And then there's you, of course,' Rachael pointed out. 'And Scott.' Not to mention Amanda, she added silently.

'I can survive anywhere. And Scott isn't in a position to dictate to me!' He was savage, blue eyes hard. 'I thought I'd put Amanda off. What happened?'

Rachael didn't like the way he avoided a discussion of his ties to the Tredegars and to Cornwall. This tough house and gale-swept heathland made him real in way the glittering world's capitals never had.

'Amanda brought the robot to cheer Tristan up. He was supposed to be ill, remember. I had to invent an allergy.'

Silas frowned, his gaze intent. 'How did she get here? She's been practically housebound for years.'

'The gardener brought her.' Rachael tried very hard not to be jealous.

Silas looked stunned but pleased. 'Wild horses wouldn't drag her into a car. I wonder why. . .?'

Rachael decided it was time to put Tristan down for a nap. The warring emotions caused by a budding friendship with Amanda Tredegar suddenly exhausted her.

'Perhaps she's tired of being wrapped in cotton wool. People with more severe handicaps have very full lives.' Turning back from the door, she explored another point that had been puzzling her. 'I gather a number of people know about the affair. You led me to believe Tristan's parentage was a secret, not common knowledge.'

Silas shrugged, loosening his tie. 'People gossip. This may be a far cry from London but people manage to count. The Tredegars look after their own; no one would be surprised by my assumption of fatherhood.'

'No, I suppose not.' Her doubts about his reasons for adopting Tristan were mirrored in her eyes. Silas Tredegar was Amanda's white knight, sacrificing all for his lady's protection. She wondered how much Silas's condemnation had made Scott consider such a convoluted arrangement.

'Before long, you'll be saying all this is my fault.' He read her thoughts with amazing accuracy.

She blushed and opened the door. 'It's time for

Tristan's nap.' Noises from the kitchen suggested the little boy was showing off his new toy to Kitty.

Silas made a dismissive gesture, watching her as she left the room, his eyes darkening with determination. Picking up the phone, he dialled a number from memory.

'Scott.' His tone was brisk. 'I suggest we meet. Amanda has been to Winterbrook.' Listening for a moment, a spasm of irritation crossed his face. 'Very well. This evening, then.' He put the receiver down without saying goodbye.

Rachael left the nursery, having placed the prized robot on top of the chest of drawers so that Tristan could see it. She felt hot and in need of a shower. Unfortunately, Winterbrook offered only a bath. Walking through the bedroom, she was grateful for the slight breeze from the open windows. Unfastening the front two buttons of her dress, she made for the bathroom, recoiling as she virtually walked into Silas.

'Oh—— Sorry,' she apologised weakly. A scalding awareness increased her temperature as she took in the towel around his waist and the damp cleanliness of his skin. 'It's hot,' she told him as if the fact was news.

'Mmm,' he agreed, his glance taking in her flustered features, his disinclination to move communicated by the relaxed stillness of his body.

'Silas,' she murmured in protest.

'What's the matter?' His voice woke unbidden memories and she found herself searching desperately for the words to back up her protest. 'I've been thinking about bringing Michael over here. The project in Exeter would be good experience. It's rather risky leaving him exposed to the more dubious pleasures of New York.'

Rachael's suspicions were legion. 'I suppose we

might as well have all our problems in one spot.' She
attempted to move past him.

He caught her arm, his jaw squared ominously. 'I
thought you might be homesick. You seem keen on
wrapping things up here.'

'No, Silas, that isn't it.' She lifted the weight of her
hair from her neck. 'Please, can I get past?'

'What would you do?' He didn't respond to her plea,
the sight of her damp hair and the scent of her heated
body making him reluctant to move. 'If this situation
resolved itself, would you go back to Geoffrey?'

'No!' She looked shocked. 'I could hardly do that.'
Pain made her eyes glitter. 'And, before you ask, I
wouldn't work for you either.'

'No,' he agreed, a glimmer of humour lightening his
eyes. 'I doubt we'd get much work done. Not now.' An
indolent finger traced the curve of one breast. 'I'd
spend my day chasing you around the desk.'

Swallowing drily, she accepted that Silas was bringing her firmly to heel. Michael was to be brought into
the equation and her need for her husband fully
exploited.

'I suppose Geoffrey would find you a bit of handful.'
His fingers indolently slipped the buttons of the dress
free, sliding inside to cup the bare curve exposed.

'You didn't like him very much, did you?' She was
so surprised by the thought that she didn't protest at
the increasing intimacy of his touch.

'And I thought you were bright.' Silas stroked her
skin, his gaze on her face, noting the dark, dreamy
depths of her eyes, the soft curves of her mouth. 'They
say love is blind,' he murmured. 'It must be true.'

'I'm not blind, Silas,' she whispered as his mouth
engulfed hers. She was ashamed at her response but
the thought of another day. . .night, close and yet not
able to touch him, made pride seem a low priority.

'You can't be in love, then.' His voice was as smooth

as silk, his breath feathering into her mouth. Shudder-
ing, she felt the tip of his tongue rub provocatively
against her teeth. 'Let me in,' he growled, his hands
moving down to her hips.

'You really don't have to do this.' Her emotional
plea got her nowhere. It even sounded weak to her
own ears; Silas wasn't averse to making love to her;
whether it was just because she was convenient she
didn't know, but his arousal wasn't in any doubt.

For an answer Silas dragged her close, one arm
around her waist, the other imperatively tipping up her
chin. His mouth fused with hers in a long endless kiss.

'One advantage of making love in the afternoon. . .'
Silas propped himself up on his elbow, watching her
lazily '. . .is that you can't disappear on me.'

Rachael wished she had the strength. Physical peace
was bought at the price of mental torment.

'You're a very sensual lady.' His dark head bent and
Rachael felt his breath against her throat, closing her
eyes as his tongue licked fire into the hollow at its base.
'Sweet as honey,' he murmured huskily, his fingers
tracing the hot, swollen peaks of her nipples. 'And very
quiet.'

Her lashes frayed apart to accuse him with passionate
intensity. Laughing softly in his throat, he read the
message in her eyes without difficulty.

'I like to hear you talk.' He kissed the rosy tip of one
breast, blue eyes wicked at her silent resentment.

Rachael turned on to her stomach, her eyes narrowing like a cat's when he appeared to find the rebuff part
of sexual play.

'You have a beautiful back.' He began to kiss his
way down her spine.

'It wasn't an invitation,' she whispered, but her
languid tone was hardly effective.

'Every time you move it's an invitation.' Lean fingers

curled over her hipbone, his jaw chafing her tender skin as he pushed her hair aside and kissed the nape of her neck. His warmth was a living testimony to temptation. 'Perhaps we should have a honeymoon.'

Rachael froze, turning on him furiously, her ringletted hair cascading over her shoulders.

'Shall we take Tristan and Michael?' she added with barely affected inspiration. Her eyes were dark with accusation. 'That would solve the problem with Scott and Amanda, wouldn't it? Darling.' Her sarcasm was unsheathed. 'You are clever.'

Silas lay back against the pillows, watching her indolently. The dark hair on his chest was damp, his skin sleek over well-toned muscles.

'Not clever enough for you, obviously.' Putting his hands behind his head, he stretched, arching his body with a lazy grace of movment that drew her reluctant gaze.

'We could always leave Tristan with Uncle Scott and Aunt Mandy,' she suggested, calling his bluff.

'Children aren't library tickets, my angel.' He was at his most unscratchable. 'Don't you like being a mother? If you don't, I suggest you tell me; you're vulnerable on that score yourself.'

A blank, non-comprehending look was followed by dawning comprehension and then something akin to horror. She had always wanted children, but to bring a child into the tangled life she led at the moment would be madness.

'Silas! Why didn't you say something earlier?'

He raised a dark eyebrow. 'I presumed you had the theory if not the practice.'

'You. . .!' She picked up a pillow and hit him with it.

Within seconds she was flat on her back with Silas above her, exulting in masculine triumph. 'What am I so guilty of, Rachael?' His fingers manacled her wrists, his lower body imprisoning her. Black hair fell forward over his forehead, giving him a piratical air. 'Making you marry me? Making you share my bed? Or possibly making you pregnant? I'm willing to take full responsibility for my actions, unlike Scott and unlike your spoilt brother Michael. So you must excuse me if I find your accusatory tone a little unjust. The fact that you resented every female I glanced at suggested you wouldn't find the deal I offered so bad. Agreed, it isn't an easy situation. . .' he took in her hostility '. . .but is it necessary to fight me every inch of the way?'

Yes, yes it was! It was the only way she could hope to remain intact. If he wanted a docile wife, willing to go along with this charade and be a substitute for the real love of his life in bed, he had definitely made a bad choice.

'I said you would get the whole woman, Silas,' she reminded him. 'You're not the one who has to deal with Amanda's curiosity. I hate all this deceit.'

'And you think I don't?' he demanded harshly. 'I did try to stop Amanda coming here—you disagreed with that. What do you want?' Silas looked exasperated. 'The only other alternative is to move. But you seem to see some dark motive behind that as well.'

She sighed, gazing at him unhappily. He was right. She was causing difficulties. The Tredegars were his problem; he was hers.

Fortunately for Rachael, the sound of Tristan's cot bars rattling saved her from having to give him an answer.

'I'll see to Tris,' Silas volunteered, his expression softening. 'I'm sorry, Rachael. I should have guessed Amanda would want to make you her friend.' Kissing her gently, he smiled. 'I seem to remember you were going to bathe when we bumped into each other.'

She smiled back, unable to resist the warmth in his eyes. Back on good terms with him, she felt ridiculously happy. She wasn't naïve enough to think it would last. Watching him leave the bed and pull on a robe, she knew that his concern for Tristan was genuine. Children entwined themselves around your heart. It would be hard for Silas to give the boy up to Scott when he thought his cousin was totally irresponsible. Sliding her legs out of bed, she decided to put the problem to the back of her mind for the time being. Silas was home and they would spend the evening together. The prospect lightened her heart and she ignored the little voice whispering, 'Fool.' She had been sensible for long enough.

They dined late that evening. Silas had been out when she had finished bathing and gone in search of him to see if he wished to discuss the plans for decorating the house. He hadn't mentioned going out but then their sojourn in the bedroom had not invited mundane chatter about the day's events. When he returned he was dressed, uncharacteristically, in black cords and T-shirt with a matching leather jacket. Restless energy emanated from him and Rachael found herself gazing at him with unguarded admiration. Blue eyes returning her interest made her hurry into speech.

'Where have you been?'

'St Ives.' He dismissed the subject and the question on her lips died. She had intended to visit the town the next day but instinct told her to avoid mentioning it. 'Have you looked at any of the samples?'

Her blank gaze told him she hadn't and he gestured to the small table laden with colour charts and wallpaper catalogues.

'You could pretend to be interested, at least.' Whatever had annoyed him seemed about to spill over and spoil their evening together.

'I've been in the kitchen preparing dinner.' She was

cool, trying to hide how much his attitude hurt her. 'Shall we look at them together?'

His mouth twisted in self-disgust. 'I'm sorry, Rachael.' He pushed his hands into his pockets, deserting her to view the fading heathland as the sky darkened. 'When I work, I pride myself on being on top of the deal. My mind works like that. I look at a problem, see all the possible angles and cover them. For business that's fine.' His low laugh was harsh and deprecatory. 'But it's not working here.'

Rachael didn't know what to say. Viewing Silas's life over the past three years—at least what she knew of it, she amended silently—told her that he kept his affairs remarkably free of complications. Was he reproaching her for deviating from the role he had cast for her or was he angry with Amanda for coming to Winterbrook and making friends with Tristan?

'People have a way of surprising you,' she agreed quietly, and swallowed drily as he swung around.

'I don't want you to surprise me.' He sounded very definite about that, his eyes holding serious intent. 'I need to be able to depend on you.'

Old faithful, she thought painfully. While Scott and Amanda indulged in their various caprices, she had to stay solid and predictable. She supposed in a family as volatile as the Tredegars someone had to be the anchorman. It brought back the reality of the situation. She had been hired for just such qualities; the fact that she had flights of fancy of her own was just tough luck. Silas didn't really want a wife, as he claimed; he wanted Rachael James, faithful secretary, dressed up to play a complex charade.

'I don't expect either of us will get what we want, Silas.' Or, she tagged on silently, what we need!

'Very cryptic. What does that mean?' He took off his jacket, slinging it over the back of the couch. 'I thought you wanted me. You've got exclusive rights;

what more could a girl want?' His dry humour saved what could have been an explosive scene.

'What more indeed?' She echoed his tone. 'Are you going to change? Or shall we eat now?'

'I'll stay as I am.' A lurking gleam in his eyes suggested that he was aware of the initial impact he had made on her and wasn't averse to exploiting it.

A dark, unbidden excitement trickled through her veins. How could she allow this desire for him to have a life of its own? When she lay satiated in his arms all manner of demands for love, commitment stormed through her, but here she was hours from the passionate interlude that very afternoon, wanting more.

'What about the study?' Silas busied himself opening a bottle of red wine. 'You seem most comfortable in there. Any ideas?'

'What? Oh!' She realised he was talking about the face-lift for Winterbrook. 'Er—peach.' She said decidedly. 'A very pale shade. With cream or magnolia woodwork. It should be a room that celebrates light. Please don't keep all that dreadful panelling.'

'Good.' He nodded, appearing to go along with her ideas. 'I agree about the light. I think we could have the windows enlarged, maybe some kind of arched effect. The wood needs replacing, so they'd have to be taken out anyway.'

Rachael found herself becoming quite enthusiastic. After their meal, they pored over the different catalogues, selecting for each of the rooms.

Silas brought her a brandy, joining her prone figure as she stretched out on the rug in front of the fire, perusing the samples of wallpapers.

'How long will it take for the structural changes to the upper rooms?' she requested absently, thanking him for the brandy.

'A month.' He eased himself down, leaning back

against one of the armchairs. 'Let's hope the good weather holds. A gale would fill the house with dust.'

She looked doubtful. 'What about Tris?'

'I've thought about that.' He was quiet for a moment. 'Do you like caravans?'

'What?' She turned, astonishment written all over her face.

'It's one way of staying in the grounds and being able to supervise the work.'

'You? Silas Tredegar, in a caravan?'

'Why not?' His eyes twinkled. 'It's very cosy. Kitty and Ted are going to Kitty's sister's. I'm having the cottage modernised for them at the same time.'

'I see.' She realised that Silas was making sure the elderly couple didn't have the strain of supervising the renovations or have to put up with the mess a bevy of workmen were bound to make. 'I think I had a more glamorous life as your secretary,' she teased him.

'Disappointed?' He lifted the brandy glass to his lips, the question casual but an air of tension about him made the laughter in her eyes die.

'You're in a strange mood, Silas. Is anything wrong?'

Swallowing the contents of his glass, he gave her a contemplative look, the masculine beauty of his face failing to offer any clue to his feelings.

'What could be wrong?' His mockery was infuriating but Rachael refused to rise to the bait.

'If you don't want to talk, I think I'll go to bed. I don't particularly like being used as a whipping boy for some problem that's bothering you.' Her dark eyes were expressive of the hurt she felt. Receiving no response except for a blank stare, she left the room, being careful not to bang the door as every instinct urged her to do.

Silas let out his breath on a long sigh. 'You are my problem, sweetheart,' he grated, getting up stiffly and replacing his glass on the drinks tray. Flexing his muscles, he glanced up at the ceiling, hearing the faint noises of his wife getting changed for bed. 'Somehow. . .' he picked up the brandy bottle '. . . I think that would be a very bad idea.' Pouring himself another brandy, he decided to wait a while before joining Rachael. Stretching his length on the couch, he listened to the sounds outside and the rattle of windows and creaks that belonged to an old house. He wondered if Winterbrook would feel the same with the old wood replaced and new paint taking away that faint musty smell.

'Maybe it will be more glamorous,' he muttered resentfully, before his mind wandered into sleep and he dreamt of being a boy again, running wild on the moors.

CHAPTER SEVEN

RACHAEL was not in the best of moods when she woke that morning. Kitty had discovered Silas sleeping in the study and had drawn her own conclusions.

'I must have fallen asleep on the couch.' Silas didn't appear to think there was anything remarkable in the event and had merely pressed a vague kiss to Rachael's forehead before departing for Exeter. He called her later to inform her that Michael, her brother, would be arriving from the States, sometime that day and that he had been booked in the Tregawney Hotel in Truro. Knowing that Newquay would have suited her brother better, Rachael reflected that Silas was not only paying Michael's gambling debts but severely clipping his wings.

Tristan decided to be difficult too. Having gathered together bucket, spade, a plastic dinghy that had to be blown up by foot-pump, beachball and a variety of clothes needed for a British summer, the little rogue refused to leave behind 'Lolly', a battered teddy bear. Leaving Tristan to Kitty's persuasion, she went in search of her own swimming-costume, guessing that the sea would be an irresistible temptation to a two-year-old and, knowing Tristan, she would have to be prepared to get wet. Quickly, she slipped on the costume, a low-backed jade slip of nylon, and pulled on a T-shirt dress with a dropped waist and gathered skirt in white and jade stripes.

Lolly was still firmly grasped in Tristan's right hand. He was waiting for her at the bottom of the stairs and she guessed he had firm instructions not to mount

them. He smiled, little white teeth showing in a perfect
line.

'Decided to be charming, now, have you, trouble?'
She took his free hand and popped into the kitchen to
say goodbye to Kitty.

'Going to seaside,' Tristan parroted happily, tugging
Rachael back towards the door.

'Have a nice time.' Kitty smiled, taking in Rachael's
summery outfit. 'You don't look more than a teenager
yourself,' she commented.

Rachael felt ninety but kept it to herself. She wondered if St Ives would fulfil the glowing references
given to it by the travelogues of the area. It was an old
fishing town, supposedly founded by St Ia or Eia, a
woman missionary from Ireland, who reputedly floated
to land on a leaf. She appreciated the Celtic imagination, even if it was drastically different from her own
very down-to-earth upbringing. Perhaps that was why
she was so attracted to Silas; he was a complex variety
of light and shadows.

Outside the house, a BMW was waiting with
accompanying uniformed driver. She bristled at the
reminder that Silas thought her an incompetent driver.

'St Ives.' She was brisk and then smiled to dispel the
look of bewilderment on the man's face. It wasn't his
fault, she chided herself. She mustn't be rude; it was
the driver's first day. Softened, she found out that his
name was Mac, short for MacDonald, and that he lived
in Truro with his wife and three children. His youngest
child was the same age as Tristan and, although a girl,
had a similar attachment to the dirtiest toy in her toy
box. It was quite pleasant for Rachael to discuss the
worries she had about Tris with someone knowledge-
able about children. By the time they reached their
destination she had become firm friends with Mac.

Arranging a time to meet, she let Mac help her on
to the beach with the paraphernalia she had deemed

necessary. The beautiful sands between St Ives and Godrevy Point were given enthusiastic approval by Tristan. He spotted another boy of a similar age and went over to inspect the sandcastle being built.

'Looks as if you'll be able to sunbathe.' Mac nodded at the pair, perspiring under his chaffeur's cap.

Rachael found the prospect very attractive. Saying goodbye, she watched Mac trudge across the sands and then spread out a beach towel, calling a reluctant Tristan back to put on the necessary sun oil and stress the importance of wearing a sun hat.

It was a beautiful day, she reflected, scanning the other inhabitants of the beach. Striped deckchairs and windshields abounded, despite the lack of wind. Older women had parted with their cardigans and further down towards the sea, where the sand was wet, a group of teenage boys were playing football. Seagulls swung in lazy arcs in a cobalt-blue sky, and the sun was high and eye-smartingly bright as it blazed down upon the largely pale-skinned population. Rachael had a permanent tan that had been topped up at various intervals during her working life with Silas. Slipping off her dress, she felt the warm stroke of sun over her shoulders. Resting her chin on her forearms, she watched Tristan digging and running about, fatigued by his seemingly inexhaustible supply of energy.

Rachael wondered what Michael would make of his summons to Cornwall. Truro would bore him silly, she knew that. He'd want to surf, sail and patronise nightclubs. She was looking forward to seeing her brother but didn't want to add defending him to the already overburdening cares she was trying to deal with at the moment. Silas was a smart operator, she acknowledged. If she displeased him, all he had to do was introduce Michael to a casino and she'd be back where she started. Could he be that callous? She swung between feeling guilty at such dark thoughts and feeling stupid because she was naïve enough to believe him innocent.

Tristan's new friend, William, stood round-eyed as Rachael gave into the demands of 'boat'. Deciding to do the decent thing and relieve William's mother, she took them both down to a sizeable pool left by the outgoing tide. Knowing that they'd capsize, she had severe reservations about the sea. Pulling on the rope attached to the front, she took them on short cruises around their private ocean, while they insisted on getting very wet as they clambered in and out. Their laughter was irresistible; Rachael found herself joining in and feeling much better for it.

Sun-pink, and sprinkled with sand, she changed Tristan into clean shorts and T-shirt before pulling her dress over her head. Mac arrived at two o'clock and carried the beach gear back to the car, while she picked up the now weary little boy.

'Where to? Winterbrook?' Mac queried. The red-headed Scotsman was clearly feeling the heat.

'I thought I'd look around the town. I'll put Tristan in the buggy. He should sleep for an hour.'

'I'll get the wife's shopping, then,' he replied gloomily, and Rachael pulled a sympathetic face. Supermarkets wouldn't be her first choice on a glorious day.

Pushing the buggy wasn't as easy as she'd thought. Tristan was a well-built little boy and St Ives had steep, winding streets. She stopped for a while in a café overlooking the harbour and sat under a canopy, sipping lemonade and eating fresh crab sandwiches. St Ives sported the much-vaunted palm trees, and with the fleet of small boats bobbling in the safe arms of the harbour it wouldn't have been out of place in Mediterranean waters.

She knew that the town was famous for its association with the art world and produced some fine pottery. Turner had painted scenes of the town and he was one of her favourite artists. Today wasn't a day for art galleries, she decided, but browsing around the craft shops appealed to her, especially with the meddlesome Tristan safely asleep.

It was rather dim-witted of her not to associate crafts with Scott but when she accidentally walked into his shop she was as surprised as he was.

'Rachael,' he greeted her with a degree of cordiality. 'I'm truly honoured.'

'Er—hello.' She glanced around the interior of the shop. It was very impressive. Scott had an artist's smock on and a pair of white shorts, thonged leather sandals making him look the part. 'I didn't know you had a shop here.'

'Didn't I mention it? I have three. One in Newquay, this one and another at Falmouth.' He walked over to where Tristan was asleep, bending to touch his cheek gently. 'Have you been on the beach?'

'Yes.' She watched the gentle gesture with sadness. 'He made a friend, and I've been towing them around in a plastic boat.' She smiled at him in a friendly manner, guessing that he would enjoy a day on the beach with his son and it must be hard to listen to second-hand reports.

'I'll make you some tea,' Scott decided. 'It's the only thing for hot summer days. Earl Grey all right?'

'Fine.'

'Look around,' he invited. 'I'll give you discount, since you're family.'

She couldn't help grinning. Scott was endearing in an odd sort of way. She wondered what Silas would think if she turned up with one of Scott's creations to adorn the revamped Winterbrook.

'Sorry if I put Silas in a bad temper last night.' He turned to see her blank look. 'Didn't he tell you he came to see me?' Scott laughed shortly. 'He plays things very close to his chest. I thought you two were as thick as thieves.'

'Obviously not.' She looked curious. 'I suppose it was about Amanda's visit?'

He nodded his shaggy head, the black hair sprinkled with silver. Blue eyes, alien yet familiar, stared demandingly into hers. 'Something about you has got him stirred up. He's different.'

Rachael doubted very much it had anything to do with her and Scott's expression relented slightly as if sensing her insecurity.

'I'm not knocking him, although the temptation is enormous.' He grinned. 'My cousin may have changed women with his socks but he hasn't had many real relationships. His childhood was school, tutors; his only real family life was here. When his mother died he was left to the tender mercy of his father. My uncle didn't like children much; he placed value on success and money. He was proud of Silas when he excelled at things but he never loved him.' Scott tapped her chin with a rough callused finger as her eyes gave her away. 'I don't know why he gets confused with you; you're easy to read.' Blushing, Rachael was glad when he turned back to the boiling kettle and poured the steaming water into a decorative teapot.

'I suppose Mandy and I were the nearest thing he had to a family. When he first came to stay here he was so clean I thought he'd jumped out of a washing powder advertisement. You have me to thank for introducing him to more masculine pursuits.'

Rachael accepted her tea. 'Were you friends?' she asked, greedy for some insight into her husband's past.

'I suppose so. He hero-worshipped me and fell in love with Amanda.' Glancing craftily at her, he smiled. 'I fell from grace; I don't know about Mandy, he's still got a soft spot for her.' Unaware of how he confirmed her worst suspicions, he looked thoughtful. 'Silas thinks

Mandy might find out about Tris. He doesn't think I'm much good at lying. That surprised me coming from Silas—his opinion of me isn't very high.'

'What did he suggest?' Rachael couldn't believe he would endorse her own opinions on the subject.

'That's the curious thing. When Mary died. . .' he stared rather fixedly into his cup of tea '. . .he wiped the floor with me. I received a set of ultimatums. I couldn't think straight. I was willing to agree to anything that seemed feasible. This time round, he was actually asking me to come up with something. I think it came down to the fact that I wasn't fit to be Tristan's father unless I could handle the situation myself.'

Rachael nodded slowly. Well done, Silas, she applauded silently. Breathtakingly simple but very effective.

'He also said if I didn't come to some decision within the next six months he would sell up Winterbrook and take Tristan to America. He's legally adopted Tris— he's quite prepared to consider him his son.'

'Oh.' Rachael was shocked at the brutality of the threat. If Scott didn't comply, he would tear both Tristan and himself from their roots and family. For a man of shadows, Silas had a way of making things very black and white.

'I thought you might want to get back to the States. This must be very different from home, for you.'

Rachael considered this. Silas wilfully misinterpreted her discomfort with the situation. If he loved her, she would follow him around the world, sleeping in a tent if need be. It was the painful lie they were all living that bothered her.

'It's difficult for me to feel that Tristan's mine,' she admitted. 'I suppose it must be hard for Silas as well, although he doesn't admit it. I don't think you're really prepared to give him up, Scott; that puts us both *in loco parentis*, not knowing if he's our child or not. Can you swear, hand on heart, that some time in the future you're not going to want to tell Tris the truth? It will be a damn sight more complicated in ten years' time than it is now.'

Scott swallowed, putting his cup and saucer down; he tried to hide the fact that his hands were shaking. 'You don't pull your punches, do you? Oh, God.' He pushed his hands through his hair, his eyes agonised. 'I don't care what hell I have to go through, it's Mandy. Can't you see how this is going to hurt her?'

Rachael's eyes mirrored his concern. There was nothing comforting she could say. Amanda Tredegar would undoubtedly be deeply upset by the whole sorry tale. Scott had an unenviable decision to make; he stood the chance of losing his wife or losing his son.

Tristan rubbed his eyes sleepily and gazed around the shop in a dazed manner, smiling when he saw the two adults.

'I'll get him a drink,' Scott volunteered while Rachael undid the safety straps on the buggy and let him out. It was a good thing Scott was prompt with the beaker of lemonade; Tristan's fascination with anything breakable made him a miniature demon in shop crammed full with exquisite pottery.

When Tristan had finished the lemonade, Rachael bade goodbye to Scott and made for her rendezvous with Mac. The day in the sunshine had tired her and by the time the buggy was folded away in the boot and Tris strapped into his safety chair she was glad to sink back into the luxuriously cushioned limousine and close her eyes.

'Mr Tredegar called,' Mac informed her. 'He said he'd be working late and he'd meet you at the Tregawney Hotel for dinner.'

'Thank you.' Rachael was not averse to putting off a meeting with Silas until then. The knowledge that he had met Scott to discuss the future and chosen not to tell her what had transpired angered her deeply. The fact that her meeting with his cousin had been by chance she didn't think he'd believe for one moment, so any discussion on the issue was bound to be acrimonious. If Michael had been summoned to England because of some misdemeanour in New York, it promised to be one hell of an evening.

Her brother, as it turned out, was in the best of spirits. He appeared to enjoy his job, had made several good friends in New York and didn't seem to be in the shadow of disgrace. He had always been keen to travel and saw his visit to Cornwall as an added perk of the job.

'Where's the boss?' he asked with a broad smile, clearly enjoying the relationship he had acquired by her marriage to his employer. Tall, with wheat-coloured hair and brown eyes, her brother was drawing the attention of several young women sitting in the hotel lounge.

'Working late.' She smiled at his obvious good spirits. 'He'll join us later. How was the trip?'

'Great. A couple of hours on Concorde, and then a helicopter ride. It certainly pays to be related to the head boy of Tredegar and Pitt.' Taking her hands, he gave her an all-encompassing glance. 'I like the outfit. How's married life?'

She was saved from replying by the sight of Greta Ibbotson, dripping costume jewellery and looking very American beside the rather more reserved English visitors to the hotel.

'Greta!' She gave the woman an enthusiastic hug. 'What are you doing here?'

'I'm not quite sure. Silas appears to be mowing through the British temp service. He sent an SOS to the office and here I am.'

The arrival of her brother and Greta Ibbotson made Rachael feel positively light-hearted. It wasn't until she was with them that she realised just how much she had missed the relaxed uncomplicated company of her friends.

Silas arrived just after nine, looking dark and handsome in a light jacket with a faint grained effect and pale beige trousers. His jaw had a shadow of stubble and with his tanned skin and vivid blue eyes he looked the epitome of masculine virility.

'How's my favourite boss?' Greta greeted him, a knowing gleam in her eyes.

'Greta.' He smiled, nodding at Michael. 'I'm sorry I'm late. Something cropped up.' Glancing at Rachael, he noted the healthy glow of a day spent in the sun, giving an added vitality to the sparkle in her eyes. 'Did you enjoy your day on the beach? You've caught the sun.' He stroked a negligent finger over her cheek.

'Yes, I enjoyed it very much. St Ives is very pretty.'

Silas gave her a keen look. 'I suppose it is. It's rather self-conscious for my taste but the tourists like it. Shall we go in for dinner?' He acknowledged the hovering waiter.

Rachael seethed with anger. So I'm a tourist. She carried on a silent battle. Not endowed with your warts-and-all approach to the beauties of Cornwall. Patronising swine!

Holding her chair for her, Silas met her eyes, reading the message there without any difficulty and hiding a smile as he sat down beside her.

'Did you come across Scott in your travels?' Silas enquired, handing around the menus and ordering the wine, after a quick consultation with the waiter and a glance around the table to see if anyone was in disagreement.

'Yes, I did. I didn't realise he had a shop in St Ives. I liked a lot of his work. But that's probably because I'm an American.' She attempted a philosophical tone.

'You did say his work was directed towards fleecing American tourists, didn't you?'

'As long as you didn't buy anything, I'll forgive you.' Silas winked at her and she tried to swallow her irritation for the sake of a harmonious evening.

Greta caught Rachael's gaze, merriment bubbling in her eyes. She loved a good spat. Michael, with his easygoing manner, noticed nothing amiss and gazed hungrily at the menu.

Silas recommended the steak Diane or the salmon with cream, which was deliciously flavoured with lemon and chives. Determined not to let Silas commandeer the evening and play big chief at the company outing, Rachael ordered the goulash. It was not the Tregawney's *pièce de résistance* but she would have eaten cardboard with enjoyment to prove that she had a voice and her compliance was not a foregone conclusion. Silas must have got the message because he studiously consulted her about the dessert with a deadpan expression that was most provoking. Irritated, she declined the sweet.

'Probably the goulash,' Silas informed the others. 'It's inclined to let down an excellent menu.'

Rachael simmered. Hot lava flowed through her veins, threatening an eruption. She managed to make adequate conversation until the meal was over. They left the table for the opulent comfort of the lounge. It was decorated with an eye to the Orient but managed to look like Aladdin's cave. It boasted a small dance floor and had a resident female vocalist with a surprisingly good repertoire of blues and soul numbers.

While the two men were at the bar ordering the drinks, Rachael and Greta had an opportunity to talk.

'Feeling homesick?' The older woman met the quick comprehending glance with a wry expression. 'Oh, that brother of yours doesn't look beyond the end of his nose but we know Silas, don't we?'

'We do,' Rachael agreed, her finger traced a pattern on the table. 'Silas thinks I'm homesick but. . . I've been away with Silas on business trips far longer than I've been in Cornwall. It isn't that.'

'Hmm.' Greta's concern was genuine. 'Finding it tough going?'

'It isn't easy.' Silas's return made her glance upwards guiltily. She was torn between loyalty to her husband and a desire to confide in someone. Perhaps it showed in her eyes; Silas took her hand and urged her to her feet.

'Come and dance,' he offered smoothly. Michael's reappearance made it impossible to refuse on the basis that Greta would be left alone.

'I'd rather details of our relationship weren't broadcast around the company. Talk to Michael if you must but not Greta.'

'I can hardly do that.' She stared fixedly over his shoulder, feeling the sweep of his gaze taking in her every expression. 'He may have been stupid but I don't think he'd like the idea that I had to get married to protect him.'

'Neither do I,' Silas replied tersely.

'The facts are unavoidable.' She was haughty.

'Are they?' He didn't sound convinced.

'You may have some strange idea that I was just waiting for you to look in my direction, but if it hadn't been for Michael's gambling debts I——'

His dark head bent, cutting off the light, and the sentence was never finished.

'I dare say pride might have got in your way,' he agreed. A smile lit his eyes at her hot, flustered indignation. The other couples on the floor regarded them with indulgence.

'You're damn right!' She glared at him, wishing her lips didn't tingle from his kiss and her traitorous body wouldn't yield quite so easily to his as they danced to the slow, hypnotic music.

'What did Scott have to say?' He changed the subject without a conscience and she gritted her teeth.

'He told me you'd been to see him. And that you intend to sell up and move out if he doesn't get his act together.'

Silas's mouth twitched in mute criticism of her short-hand version of the terms he had given his cousin. 'You wanted something done. I thought you'd be pleased. You agree the situation can't continue.'

'Yes.' She didn't elaborate. If Silas was going to go it alone, she didn't intend to applaud.

'But. . .' he prompted.

'I can't think why you're consulting me. It's not your usual style.' Her sarcasm was accompanied by dark, glittering resentment as she met his eyes. 'Despite a touching bout of confusion the other night, you still seem to think you can run your personal relationships along the same line as Tredegar and Pitt. It's doubly convenient when you can bring in your employees to soothe the troubled waters at home.'

His lazy regard made her toes curl. 'I don't like to see you unhappy.'

The gurgle of laughter that broke from her throat echoed her derision. 'Why, Silas, I didn't know you cared.'

'Hey!' He touched her cheek and she pulled away from his touch, unable to endure the torment of his lukewarm emotions. To be liked was an insult when you craved for love.

'Six months isn't a lifetime, Rachael.' His eyes hardened perceptibly. 'If you get your wish, Tris will go to Scott and Amanda. In that eventuality you can make your own decisions about the future. I can't force you to stay with me. Financially——'

'I don't want any of your money!' Eyes smarting, she

pulled out of his arms. Fortunately the number had come to an end and her departure from the dance-floor went unnoticed.

Silas caught up with her, shackling her wrist with his fingers. 'We're going home,' he stated grimly.

'You can go home if you like.' She flashed a rebellious glare at his stiff features. 'Since we've established that Michael and Greta are here for my amusement, I shall enjoy their company. I've had enough of yours to last me a lifetime!' She felt great relief in being hideously rude. 'Why don't you go home? I'll be careful not to wake you. If I'm very late, I'll sleep in the study.'

'I have no intention of leaving without you,' he informed her coolly.

'Then you'll have a long wait.' Eyes over-bright, she noted the raised tempo of the music and urged her brother on to the dance floor. She felt in a wild mood and wanted to get as far away from Silas as possible. His every word provoked her and if she wasn't careful she had visions of herself striking him in full view of all those assembled in the lounge of the Tregawney Hotel.

'Rachael's a good dancer,' Greta commented, amused by her employer's black temper. He was literally scowling, a rare show of expression for a man usually difficult to read.

He didn't reply, his eyes never leaving his wife's sinuous form, his expression hawklike when one of the young men on the dance-floor started to pay her attention.

'Looks as if you've got competition.' Greta bit into a crisp and then subsided when he put a finger to his lips. She knew when Silas meant it—she had been working for him for a long time. Rachael sure was cooking up a storm of trouble, she reflected, as the younger woman changed partners and Michael pursued his own interests.

Rachael had always enjoyed dancing and found a welcome relief in the pounding music. Peter

Buckingham, the young salesman she was dancing with, was celebrating making his sales target and seemed in a similar hedonistic mood. He had asked her if she was with anyone, spotted the ring and was happy to settle for a dance partner.

When Michael returned to the table, he glanced back at his sister, laughing at her sheer exuberance. His grin died as Silas eyed him coldly.

'Would you like to fetch your sister back to the table?' His voice had icicles in it.

'She's just having fun.' Michael was puzzled at his brother-in-law's attitude.

'Just do it.' Silas's voice was soft with menace. Michael was halfway to the dance-floor before he knew it.

Rachael welcomed her brother, moving to accommodate him in the restricted amount of space. Peter Buckingham, under the impression she was being reclaimed, bowed out gracefully.

'Whew.' She took in a deep breath. 'What are you looking so serious about?'

'Silas is getting pretty heavy. He wants you back pronto.'

'What?' Rachael glanced at the table, her face sobering for a moment. 'Oh, he probably has to get up early tomorrow morning. Stay and dance. I don't feel like sitting down.'

Michael looked awkward. 'I—er—I think he might make a scene. . .'

'Silas!' She chuckled at the thought. Silas playing the jealous lover was quite a thought. Scenes weren't Silas's *modus operandi*. Cold disapproval, now, that he was good at.

'Rachael,' Michael warned. 'Greta and I, well, he's our boss and you're my sister. . .'

Don't make waves, she interpreted, wondering if Michael would find it palatable to discover just how many waves he had made and who was manning the lifeboat. With a toss of her head, she walked back to the table, her long, slender legs revealed in small glimpses by the provocative split in her skirt.

Silas watched her approach, a glint of admiration in his gaze at the proud tilt of her chin and the mutinous sparks in her eyes.

'You called, master.'

'Take a day to settle in.' Silas ignored her insolence, speaking instead to their guests. Standing up to join Rachael, he handed her her evening bag, the warning in his gaze quelling.

'We'll have lunch some time.' Greta glanced from one to the other with avid curiosity.

'Yes, I'll call you.'

After brief goodbyes, Rachael found herself being steered towards the exit with barely controlled impatience. The warm evening air was soft and intoxicatingly pure after the smoke in the hotel.

'Is something wrong, Rachael?' Silas's tone was barely polite. 'You've been in an aggravating mood all evening.'

She regarded him steadily over the hood of the car as he approached her to open the passenger door.

'I can open it myself.' She dismissed the ritualistic chivalry that in her experience often cloaked overt male chauvinism. Considering that Silas had been in a particularly patronising mood for most of the evening, she was not amenable to empty gestures of value.

'What is it?' he enquired with thinning patience. 'Michael being here, Scott or the Hungarian goulash?'

Rachael strapped herself in, didn't trust herself to speak and gave him a blast from her eyes that spoke volumes.

'I see.' He fired the ignition, a muscle flexing in his jaw, his blue eyes narrowed as he negotiated the exit to the car park. 'Feel free to express yourself. I'm willing to listen.'

'You talk a lot,' she offered tightly. 'You'd make a good politician; not much content but a lot of syrup.'

It was his turn to glare. 'Am I to take it that the exhibition on the dance-floor was some kind of statement? A protest of some kind?'

'No,' she snapped back. 'The goulash was a protest. I enjoy dancing; I'm sorry if you object.'

'It sounds like it,' he returned sourly.

They settled into a truculent silence which both seemed at pains not to break. Winterbrook appeared out of the darkness, forbidding granite lightened by a small porch light. Rachael idly softened the house with imaginary wistaria and a white wood porch before she dismissed the idea. She had no part in Winterbrook. She wondered if time was running out for Silas as well. Would he return to his home if Scott and Amanda made up their differences and formed a family unit with Tristan. It was hardly surprising he had disapproved of her interference; Amanda's white knight was likely to lose his quest.

Rachael got ready for bed, hearing the sounds of Silas checking the house, wondering if he would join her or end up sleeping on the couch again. Six months! Scott could decide to let Tristan go to America but she didn't believe that he would and neither did Silas. So, within six months, she and Silas would go their separate ways. Unbearable though the situation was, the thought of never seeing Silas again filled her with anguish.

The sound of the telephone ringing and then stopping abruptly as it was answered explained Silas's failure to appear. Drifting off to sleep, Rachael was unaware of her husband entering the bedroom or his movements around the room as he got ready for bed.

Rachael woke several hours later, kicking off the covers and feeling unbearably hot. The open windows offered the tease of coolness but she was still burning up. Half asleep, she pulled off her nightdress and breathed a sigh of relief.

Outside the night sky was purple, lightening towards the east. She could hear the sound of sheep bleating in the distance and the crows that resided in the ancient trees at the end of the garden. The awakening dawn called to her senses, the burning restlessness crawling like static electricity over her skin. Silas moved, his hand sliding over her stomach to cover her hip. She turned her head to look at him. His eyes were closed, his face all lean angles in the subdued light. Unable to stop herself, she touched his cheek, letting the pads of her fingers run over the shadow of stubble on his jaw. She couldn't help it. However annoyed or hurt he made her feel, he had an overpowering attraction for her that transcended dignity, pride or even a desire for self-protection.

When he didn't wake, she became bolder. Silas slept without the adornment of pyjamas and she had left him uncovered when she kicked the sheet away. Sliding her hand over his, where it rested on her hip, she explored the bones at his wrist, moving over his forearm, the tickle of hair causing her to repeat the sensation before sweeping over his bicep to the smooth, hard warmth of his shoulder.

'Is this a private party or can anyone join in?' The husky tone of Silas's voice made her start guiltily.

'I'm sorry.' She felt suddenly very embarrassed and very naked.

'Why?' The word hung in the air between them as she gazed into his eyes, mesmerised by the heat of arousal he didn't attempt to hide. 'I like you touching me, that can't be a secret.' His hand came up to cup her cheek. 'Is the heat keeping you awake?'

'Yes.' She swallowed. His thumb caressed her ear and she shivered, the delicious sensation making her want him to run his hands all over her body and give her that wild pleasure, exploding in her veins.

'This isn't going to make you feel any cooler.' Amusement threaded the dark, velvety tone of his voice but his lips cut off any response Rachael could make. Protest would have been useless; it was what she wanted and her arms wound around his neck, her lips parting under his firm persuasion, her tongue moving in silken seduction against the forceful pressure of his. He drugged her with his kisses, the skilful play of his hands over her skin. His mouth moved hotly to her throat and she moaned, moving restlessly as he bit at the tender join of her neck and shoulder, making her squirm beneath him and dig her fingernails into his flesh in revenge.

'Get your nails out of my skin.' Blue eyes blazed down into hers, a fiery challenge between them that threatened to get out of control.

'You bit me.' She let her fingers trail down his back, watching his throat arch as he felt her feline claws.

'You're lucky that's all I did. I could have cheerfully strangled you tonight.'

'Why? Because I was enjoying myself?' She hadn't expected to escape retribution.

'I don't like you flirting with other men. Despite your charming modesty, you must know how it is between us.' Black hair shadowed his forehead, leaving his eyes unrevealing, but the hard angles of his cheekbones and jaw conveyed the depth of feeling well enough.

'I wasn't flirting,' she denied hotly. 'I suppose you're used to those voracious gold-diggers fawning over your every command. I am not like that!'

His derisive laughter made her glare up at him, every inch of her burning in accusation. What Silas saw was a passionate, naked woman, with only him for cover. Rachael made a choked sound of fury when his gaze dropped to the fullness of her creamy breasts, the golden tan of her chest fading where the minute protection of her bikini kept off the sun. Silas had no such compunction; his lean flanks were as bronzed as the rest of him. He let his weight rest against her, the soft harbour of her loins cushioning the masculine hardness of his.

'I've met women less complicated about their desires.' He spoke through barely moving lips, his mind absorbed with the feeling he was creating between them.

Rachael clutched at his arms with some self-defeating intention of refusing him and their eyes clashed in a fury of wanting.

'It's too hot to fight.' Silas brushed her lips with his, his exploration sweeping down over her chin to the vulnerable underside of her jaw.

Trying desperately to keep her head and make a shape of the burning injustice she felt, she took in a drag of warm, humid air. The smell of baked earth and sweet gorse perfumed the night in an intoxicating scent. She felt the warm tide of Silas's breath against the curve of her breast. Her nipples were rigid as if cold, the teasing touch of his tongue making her gasp, her body arching. Capturing her wrists, he raised them above her head, so that they lay on the pillow. Sliding his hands down the paler underarms, he cupped her breasts, meeting the resentful daze she was in with an air of triumphant mastery. And didn't he love to be in control? Rachael felt her whole body blush as his strong fingers massaged her breasts. She was stretched out for his delectation like a slave girl and he was revelling in every minute of it.

'You can always tell me what you want.' His voice was smoky with desire and the teasing lash against her nipple made the aroused crest scream for more. With a swift shove, Rachael had him flat on his back and his blue eyes laughed back at her, although there was fire in his gaze.

'Yes, my lady?' His voice silked over her nerve-ends and then his hands gripped just below her armpits, lifting her above him, his mouth closing hard over the tortured peak of her breast, causing Rachael's head to fall back and a purely feminine groan to issue from her lips. It was a Pyrrhic victory, she realised; she couldn't beat him at love games because he was quite happy in defeat. When he finally let her settle against his strong, aroused body, she covered his chest in kisses, displacing the black silky hair with her tongue, tracing the edge of his ribcage, the plain of his stomach tensing as her slim fingers went on their own particular quest, determined to drive the man she loved as crazy as he did her.

'Rachael. . .' The driven note to his voice thrilled her. His hands entangled in her hair, shaping her skull.

'What?' She peeped up at him, only to be hauled up against him and turned under him on to the sheet. His body surged against hers and their mouths met in heated collision.

Sparks flew through Rachael's body in a firestorm of pleasure. Her fingers dug into the curve of Silas's shoulders, her loins absorbing the impact of his thrusting body, quivering and waiting anew. Of their own volition her legs wrapped themselves around him. It was as if she wanted to absorb him into her very soul and keep him there. Love burnt out all nice emotions; she needed to know he was hers, possess him so deeply that she was free to trust, free of torment.

'Easy. Stay with me,' Silas breathed into her neck, but she was beyond him and she cried out softly into the night as the pleasure twisted and racked her body, the hot earth scent mingling with the damp heat from their bodies. Silas rested on his arms, his face locked in a mask of male need, a hoarse shudder of air taken in as if he was drowning as he made one last, hard penetration of her womanhood before sinking into the warmth of her arms.

It was a quiet time between both of them. Rachael could feel the heavy thud of Silas's heartbeat and hear the faltering rhythm of his breathing. She felt languid and drowsy, the tenderness of her body tingling in a manner that wasn't unpleasant.

'And you're going to leave me, are you?' Silas propped himself up on one elbow, his hips still imprisoning hers. Tracing her lips, he viewed the sensual relaxation of her mouth and the lack of flight in her eyes with some satisfaction. 'I wonder how far you'll get?'

'Do you care?' she asked, leaving herself open to be wounded.

'Yes.' His head dipped as he kissed her softly. 'I need you.'

Rachael was sure that was true. Beside the Tredegars she was all he had, one of the few people who had seen beyond the charming charade, with the added advantage that she didn't make him vulnerable.

'You need me too.' He kissed her again with more intensity. Rachael decided not to argue; Silas could quite adequately compensate her for keeping the peace and she linked her arms around his neck, sighing her delight as his hard, very male body pressed her back against the sheet.

CHAPTER EIGHT

RACHAEL responded to Tristan's demand to be 'up' and Kitty joined them at the window to watch the six-berth caravan being sited at the end of the garden.

'It's big enough, I suppose.' Kitty sounded dubious. 'I'm surprised you're not going to a hotel.'

So was Rachael, but then Tristan would find hotel life restrictive and it did help to be 'on site'. Workmen, she knew from her extensive work in the development field, had a very imaginative interpretation of the plans if left to their own devices. A temporary fence was to be erected to make sure Tristan couldn't get anywhere near the fascinating machines to be used.

Silas came into the kitchen and waved in the general direction of the van. 'Want to have a look?'

Tristan wriggled to be 'down' and Rachael winked at Kitty. 'Well, that's two enthusiasts.'

'They don't have to cook and clean,' Kitty summed up the disadvantages, watching the trio as they left the house and reappeared seconds later on the lawn. They made an attractive family group. She smiled fondly after them.

'Well, what do you think?' The idea of the holiday home seemed to appeal to Silas.

'Is this some thwarted boyhood ambition?' Rachael queried with a smiling glance.

Silas grinned sheepishly. 'Apart from times at Winterbrook, I had a very organised childhood. I used to envy the kids who camped out. You don't mind, do you?'

'No.' She viewed the fridge and quite adequate cooker and decided it was, in terms of modern living,

143

rather more luxurious than the present state of Winterbrook House. As she had been born on a farm, Rachael's holidays had been spent with cousins living in the city. She thought the caravan might be quite fun.

Tristan was bouncing on the bench seats that were set back against the rear of the van that acted as a lounge. They were still covered with plastic, which made a satisfactory crunching noise. Casting her eyes up to the ceiling in mock horror, Rachael opened one of the inner doors to discover a bedroom with a double bed. A small wardrobe and shelves provided storage space but apart from that there wasn't room for much else.

'It has all the basic essentials.' Silas came up behind her, his hands sliding down her ribs to her hips and drawing her back against him. She looked cool in the baggy white T-shirt she wore with a long turquoise side-buttoned skirt but Silas's close proximity made her feel anything but.

'Have they decided when they're going to start yet?' She turned to face him but he didn't move back, merely regarded her with a leisurely air.

'Monday,' he revealed, smiling at her surprise. 'The head of this outfit, Paddy McMahon, wants some of the Exeter work. I think we can depend on speed and good workmanship, don't you?'

'Mmm. You think of everything.' Her voice was not without criticism and a dark eyebrow queried her tone.

'Someone has to,' he returned with equal subtlety of undertone.

Voices outside the caravan made Silas glance past her and she saw him frown. 'Scott,' he muttered, and the pound of small feet made it clear that Tristan had heard too.

'And Amanda,' Rachael murmured, following him out of the caravan and adopting a pleased smile.

'Hello, you two.' Amanda hung on to her husband's

arm and then amended it to 'three' as Tristan virtually catapulted into them.

'Have the share prices dropped?' Scott was provocative as usual, eyeing the caravan with amusement.

'I don't make bad investments,' Silas returned smoothly and his cousin grinned at the gibe.

'You could have stayed with us,' Amanda offered with divine innocence. 'We have plenty of room.'

'Silas wants to be near the house,' Rachael explained, glancing at his unrevealing profile. 'Would you like a drink?' She waved towards the garden furniture and they moved to the white ironwork table and chairs.

'I've come to invite you to a dinner party.' Amanda smiled at them both, her eyes sparkling with anticipation. 'It's the first one I've had for years. . . Well, since the accident really.' She put her hand over Scott's and they shared a long look. 'I'd like you both there because you're my favourite people and I need moral support.'

Refuse that if you dared! Rachael waited tensely for Silas to reply but he merely smiled and nodded. 'We'd be delighted. When?'

'A week next Saturday. You'll be in the caravan then. It would probably be for the best if you stayed overnight. Tristan will be asleep when the party's over; it would be a shame to disturb him.'

'Fine,' Silas agreed again, his eyes skimming over Scott, who was diplomatically watching the antics of a blackbird at the end of the garden.

Rachael decided to retreat and fetch cold drinks. Amanda was spreading her wings like an injured bird regaining its strength and Scott was struggling to reveal his past, a burden that might prove too much for her. She was beginning to share Silas's forboding, but what else could be done? Amanda's new-found sociability had its own dangers if gossip was rife about Tristan's parentage. A few careless words would reveal Scott's guilty secret. She felt like a character in Shakespearian tragedy, where everything marched on until the plot culminated in mayhem.

Silas was strangely reticent about the invitation and Rachael wondered why. He had given Scott a six-month time limit to get his affairs in order and he seemed willing to go along with any overture being made to forge links between Tristan and his prospective parents.

'Are you worried about taking Tristan to Scott's?' she asked him, but he merely shrugged.

'Not as worried as Scott is.' He was dismissive and the subject was dropped. Later she watched him play with Tristan in the garden. He was pretending to be a monster and Tristan's excited face made her laugh. Amanda was right, the youngest Tredegar was a heartbreaker; she would miss him deeply when. . . Shaking off the cold feeling that ran from the tips of her toes to the roots of her hair, she turned to see Kitty. The woman had been watching her, a fact she hastily tried to disguise.

'What's the matter, Kitty?' She responded to some trouble she felt in the woman.

'Oh, nothing. Well. . .' She went to put the kettle on, her bustling figure never really still. 'It's just moving out, I suppose. I feel as if things won't be the same ever again.'

'I don't suppose it will take you long to get used to central heating and a fitted kitchen,' Rachael responded lightly, but she knew that wasn't what the older woman meant. It would take a month for Winterbrook to be habitable again and it was impossible to predict what would happen in that time.

The workmen arrived, as predicted, on Monday morning. They had the appearance of a wrecking crew, their task to knock down the partition walls of some of the smaller rooms on the upper floor and make them into decent-sized bedrooms. There would be six bedrooms in all when the work was completed. Downstairs, the plan was for two reception-rooms, a dining-room, study and a modernised kitchen with breakfast-room overlooking the gardens at the back. It was hard to imagine the finished product but then Rachael had seen sites, nothing more than wastelands, turned into shopping centres, luxury flats and leisure centres. In a few months' time it would be hard to remember the old Winterbrook with its draughts and dark Victorian furnishings. It was a sad thought that, whatever happened, Silas might no longer wish to live in his family home and their present efforts would be for the benefit of strangers.

Greta came upon Rachael, dressed in a pair of dungarees and a T-shirt, covered in dust. She was taking a sub-contractor through the plans.

'Maybe it is a problem.' She confronted the patronising boss of the outfit who was overseeing the work to be done. 'But it's my understanding that Mr McMahon wants some part of the Exeter project. . .'

'I'm not working for McMahon.' He was slightly less belligerent in attitude now. 'I'm not causing problems, Mrs Tredegar; we have to make sure the building is safe. There are a lot of structural alterations——'

'Which were all discussed with the architect. Nothing changes.' She remained stubborn, knowing that although George Peters worked for himself he was still reliant on McMahon for part of the action. Catching sight of her friend, she left the man glowering behind her.

'Making friends?' Greta wise-cracked, her voice lowered so they wouldn't be overheard.

'How did you guess?' Pushing her hands through her hair, Rachael moved away from where the men were working. 'Tris is visiting his grandparents today.

They're going on a day trip on Friday, which is their usual day for seeing him.' It seemed a good idea all round for Tristan to be out of the way while the workmen tackled the heavier work. 'So you can have lunch without being pounced on. Have you got the day off?'

'Uh-huh.' Greta accompanied her out of the house to the caravan. 'Silas has gone to Paris. He said he'd ring if he can't get back tonight.'

'Oh.' Paris jolted her. It brought back unwelcome memories of Silas's words about her not being the type to take on a fling to Paris. She wondered if she would still be found wanting if he ever took her to the world's capital of romance.

'He seemed to think he'd get back home before nightfall.' Greta misinterpreted her concern. 'It doesn't take long by helicopter.'

'No, of course not.' Hastily she changed the subject. 'Are you still at the Tregawney or has he moved you to somewhere in Exeter?'

'I don't think I'm really here to work.' She gave Rachael an old-fashioned look. 'Michael and I are staying put. We have Mac to drive us to work every morning. You should be flattered. Silas is obviously desperate to keep you happy.'

Rachael smiled artificially and stood up, eager to escape from any discussion on Silas's supposed devotion. 'Would you like coffee?' Searching for the ground coffee, she spooned some of the rich dark granules into the filter machine.

'I never thought I'd see Silas jealous.' Greta was tenacious. 'Boy, was he mad the other night when you were dancing with that guy at the hotel. When Michael came back without you, he was lethal.' She shivered dramatically. 'I never thought he had it in him. He's always so urbane,' she reminisced.

'Silas has hidden qualities.' Rachael left the machine

to work its magic and looked dubiously at her clothes. 'I'd better have a quick shower and get changed. Do you mind?'

'No, go ahead.' Greta picked up a magazine that had been left on the fold-away table, quite willing, it seemed, to make herself at home.

Rachael showered in the small cubicle, washing away the grime from the house, but unfortunately found her troubles a little harder to shift. The ongoing argument in her head was driving her crazy. If Amanda was forever forbidden to Silas, he would be a faithful, considerate husband. On the plus side, he needed her, he was willing to admit that. On the minus side, he didn't love her. Oh, in time he might grow to love her, shared memories and perhaps children drawing them together, but it would never be that dynamic, ecstatic love of true lovers. She was Rachael; dependable, good-hearted Rachael. There were worse things to be but she was unbearably hurt by coming second best. She didn't know if she could handle that, even for Silas.

Distracting Greta from the subject of her husband, Rachael showed her the plans for the house and they pored over the sketches Rachael had made to show the decorators. On every drawing a small piece of wallpaper showed the pattern to be used and a colour chart showed the choice of colour. They had intended to hire an interior decorator but found they had so many ideas between them that another vision, even if it was artistically motivated, might over-complicate things.

'I like the kitchen,' Greta enthused, viewing the cabinetmaker's photographs of his work and approving of the cherrywood chosen for its light but rich colour. White tiles with a small mosaic in the centre of every set of four gave detail without being dominant. They were keeping the Aga stove because they both liked it and had been maintaining the fantasy that they would live in the house when the plans were made.

Amanda called in while they were washing the dishes after lunch and made Greta's acqaintance. Discovering that both Rachael's brother and the redoubtable Greta were newcomers to the country, they immediately became added to her invitation list. If Rachael's heart had been capable of sinking lower, it would have done.

'She's beautiful.' Greta watched her depart, holding on to the gardener's arm for support. 'Rumours are rife about her husband in the Exeter office.' Catching Rachael's swift glance, she nodded in answer to the question in her eyes. 'Silas has recruited firms from around here to work on the site. He does it whenever he can; regional loyalty, I suppose. They say that Scott Tredegar had more to do with this Deal woman that Silas. And it isn't really Silas's style, is it? He always kept it light, dabbling with rich socialites who knew the score.'

Rachael sighed deeply, drying her hands. 'I didn't realise Tristan's parentage was being discussed as far away as Devon.' She was dry.

'I'm not being nosy. . . Well, I can't help being curious. I didn't realise a child was involved until the Tredegar and Pitt grapevine dished the dirt.' Greta was incorrigible. 'The reason why I mentioned it was to let you know what's going on. Michael went white when he heard the gossip. I guess he was angry at people for discussing family business.'

Rachael cringed. Oh, dear! Had Michael finally seen beyond his own self-interest and realised that sacrifices had been made on his behalf? He had known that Silas had settled his debts but had taken it as a gesture of goodwill from his rich brother-in-law, on the understanding that he mended his ways. How would the idea his sister had sacrificed her freedom sit on his shoulders? she wondered.

Michael had, it turned out, taken this new appraisal of his situation very hard. Not long after Greta had gone, he arrived at the caravan, looking the way Rachael felt. His blond hair was ruffled, his eyes heavy with concern. He sat in awkward silence while she put Tristan's tea in front of him and refused to join them when she invited him to do so.

'What's the matter?' she asked quietly, and received a burning look.

'I'm waiting to speak to Silas. I think you know what about.'

She raised an eyebrow, gentle humour lurking in the depths of her eyes. 'Do I?'

'Yes.' His eyes flashed, then he glanced at Tristan and lowered his voice. 'I think you married Silas so that he would pay what I owed! How could you do that, Rachael? How could he make you!'

Tristan studied Michael but solemnly munched his way through a sandwich.

'It wasn't like that,' she lied. 'We both had problems; we merely decided to solve them in a very practical way. I suppose you would have preferred Dad to take on the burden of your debts?' she put the record straight in case he was developing any romantic illusions about being a man done wrong.

'No, of course not.' He blushed to the roots of his hair. 'But your—er—relationship, well, it's hardly platonic. Anyone can see that just looking at the pair of you. I don't like to think that——'

Rachael chuckled, her brother's agony of embarrassment igniting her sense of humour.

'Well, don't think it, then. Silas is a very attractive man. Our relationship is built on a certain amount of expediency but I suppose you could say that about a lot of marriages. At least ours is honest.' She picked a banana out of the fruit bowl and peeled it for Tristan, smiling as he said 'Ta'. 'Please don't bother Silas with this tonight. He'll have had a hard day. If he gets back from Paris, the last thing he'll want is a family trauma.'

Michael tried hard to hide the fact that he was relieved. From what he had heard and witnessed himself, Silas wasn't someone to tangle with.

'Oh, by the way. . .' She found she was getting a dab hand at changing the subject. 'Amanda Tredegar has invited Greta and your good self to her dinner party on Saturday. It will be full evening garb, I guess for around eight o'clock. I'll let you know for certain during the week.'

'That should be fun.' Michael eyed her knowingly. 'Mom and Dad don't know about Tristan, do they? Why didn't you tell them?'

'I have my own reasons, which for the moment I'd like you to respect.' She was serious, and that had a powerful impact on her essentially weaker brother.

'All right. I owe you that. Why do I get the impression things aren't permanent around here? You've changed, Rachael. This whole set-up isn't like you.'

That was certainly true. Was she becoming cynical about love and marriage? It had been a cherished dream from being a little girl, watching weddings under a blue Iowa sky, seeing the happy, smiling faces, the colours, the tears, the thrown bouquet. For a moment she felt all the frustrations of the past couple of months rise up within her. She would never be the same again. The thought left her feeling hollow and sad.

Micahel stayed until Silas returned, not liking to leave her alone, unprotected in a caravan, miles away from the nearest house. He left after exchanging the usual pleasantries and Rachael was left alone with her husband, wondering how much of the day's events she should divulge.

Deciding to tell him that Amanda's dinner party had increased by two, she was surprised how little interest he showed in the affair. He had a shower, donned a bathrobe and peeped in on Tristan, watching the little boy sleep.

'I swore I'd let nothing hurt him.' He spoke almost to himself but Rachael overheard and a lump came into her throat.

Pouring him a stiff whisky, she put it down on the table and approached him quietly. Tristan's black hair and nose could be seen above the duvet, his cheeks pink, flushed with sleep.

'The light will wake him.' She drew Silas away and he met her concerned gaze, his own haunted.

'I wouldn't trust Scott with my watch, never mind. . .a child.' He picked up the whisky, a half-laugh breaking from his lips. 'I nearly said "my son". I love that kid.' He drank the whisky in one, and put the glass down, blue eyes suddenly engulfing her in a wash of hectic emotion. 'I suppose that never occurred to you when you were busy carving a path out of here.'

Rachael bent her head, the light gleaming on the burnished crown. 'He's your nephew, Silas. You can still love him. You can have children of your own— Amanda can't.'

'Amanda,' he repeated grimly. 'Let's hope she falls in with all this after a decent interval of tears and reproach. I don't suppose she's got much choice, her self-esteem is about zero.'

Rachael swallowed drily. 'You care very deeply about Amanda, don't you? I'm sure you'll be able to help her, if no one else can.'

Silas hooked a finger under her chin, his black lashes shadowing his eyes, his mouth thin with displeasure. 'And how do you suggest I do that? You seem to have forgotten—I've shielded Scott for the last two years, it's hardly likely to make me a hot favourite for confidant, is it? And who else has she got? This charade was supposed to protect her. The way things are turning out, its going to leave her stranded and more vulnerable than ever.'

So, Rachael summed up, she was to blame for upsetting the apple-cart. Silas could handle the deceit when he thought it was protecting Amanda. When it looked like casting him in the guilty role, he found his position more onerous.

'I'm sure Amanda will understand that you had her best interests at heart.' Her tone was less than conciliatory. 'Of course, she might resent both of you on the grounds that she is a fully grown woman and not a child to be manoeuvered by men who presume they know better.'

Silas glared at her, his black eyebrows drawn together in a thunderous scowl. 'It might interest you to know that Amanda was on the edge of a nervous breakdown when Tristan's mother died. She is in the peak of health now, in comparison to that.'

'That puts her in the minority.' Rachael had reached the end of her tether. 'Because the rest of us are going crazy with this situation. There's no way this is going to remain a secret, Silas. They're gossiping about Scott and Mary Deal in your Exeter office. The only way we can protect Amanda from the truth is to put her under house arrest. So don't blame me for ruining things for you; it would have happened anyway.'

A silence followed her words, the tension between them vicious and raw. Tristan's snores reached them from his contented sleep, ludicrously incongruous. Rachael found herself smiling and then laughing, a small, strained husky laugh. 'God, I'll miss him too.'

Silas swallowed hard, a muscle shifting in his jaw. 'Have you thought about what might happen if Amanda refuses to accept Tristan? He'll still need you then.'

Rachael hadn't contemplated anything of the sort. She felt, deep in her bones, that such a possibility wouldn't occur. Rubbing her forehead, she realised she was developing a full-blown headache. Not surprising really, after the day she'd had.

'What's the matter?' Silas smoothed the spot she had rubbed with his thumb, repeating the gesture when her eyes closed in appreciation.

'Just a headache,' she mumbled, as a soft kiss made her feel infinitely better if not something of a fraud. They were in the middle of a fight and some instinct urged her that it should be fought to the bitter end.

'Go to bed. I'll fetch you a warm drink and some aspirin,' he promised, turning her gently and urging her in the direction of the bedroom. She was grateful to go.

She must have been asleep by the time Silas joined her. She had vague memories of snuggling into his warm body and being accepted in his embrace but she awoke alone to the feeling of intense discomfort. Her throat was sore, her head was pounding and Tristan was bouncing on the end of her bed.

'I suppose you want breakfast,' she croaked, getting up and groaning as she swung her legs out of bed. She really did feel awful.

'How's life in a tin can?' Scott turned up just before lunch much to the relief of a bored Tristan. 'Dear me. You do look under the weather.'

'I feel terrible,' she informed him hoarsely; her eyes felt as if they had lead weights attached and she just wanted to sleep.

'Hmm, there's a virus going around. It looks like you've caught it. Do you want me to entertain the little monster for a few hours? I wouldn't mind a bit.' His smile was all boyish charm.

She looked at the sky rather dubiously. Dark clouds were gathering to the west and the wind had freshened to a stiff breeze. 'I think we're in for a storm.'

'It won't break for a few hours,' Scott predicted and

she gave in to his greater knowledge of local weather conditions.

'All right, but don't go far,' she cautioned. Even though Silas was trying to accept the idea of Tristan's living with his father, she didn't imagine he'd like the idea of Scott having access to the child on a casual basis. It didn't go with his all-or-nothing approach. Only her concern for the boy's safety allowed her to agree to Scott's suggestion. She was desperately trying to keep awake; the fear of sleeping and leaving Tristan to his own devices in the caravan terrified her.

When Scott returned, she gazed blearily at him from where she was lying on the bed. She knew who he was and that Tristan must be somewhere but her mind seemed to have a clamp on it and instead of getting up she laid her head down again.

When she woke, she was in an unfamiliar bedroom with all hell breaking loose outside.

'It's only the storm,' a female voice that was familiar told her. 'Don't worry about Tris; he's had his supper and he's going to bed in half an hour. Silas knows you're here. He's staying in Exeter overnight—the roads are flooded and people are being advised not to travel.'

'Oh. Where am I?'

'Thornfield.' The voice had a gentle chuckle in it.

'Is that Amanda?' She tried to open her eyes but the room was too bright and she shut them again.

'Yes. Now go to sleep. The doctor said that was the best thing. There's nothing to worry about. Everything's under control.'

'I wish it were,' she mumbled and drifted back into sleep.

She slept more than she was awake for the next three days. She had lucid patches and others where she was caught up in waking dreams that preyed on her worst fears. Rising panic seemed to carry her on a wave of terror until she tumbled into a safe place where a voice comforted and soothed her.

Silas lifted Rachael out of bed, placing her carefully on the camp-bed he had been sleeping on, and moved to help Amanda put on fresh sheets.

'She's still feverish.' His voice was tense and Amanda smiled at him across the bed.

'The doctor said there was a fever in some cases. Rachael's healthy; he didn't anticipate any complications. I'm sure she'll be fine in a couple of days.'

'Yes.' He took one of the pillows and straightened, stripping the damp pillowcase and replacing it with a clean one. He looked strained, the skin taut over his angular bone-structure, his black hair making his skin look sallow.

'You didn't sleep last night, did you?' Amanda chided him, sounding concerned. 'Do you want me to take over tonight, so that you can rest?'

'No.' He smiled quickly to apologise for the abruptness of his tone. 'She's in a strange country—a strange house. The least I can do is be here for her.'

'All right.' Amanda watched him as he went over to the camp-bed and bent over the American woman.

'It's all right, sweetheart,' he comforted her, as she protested at the disturbance.

Rachael's eyes frayed open to stare at him, trying to make sense of the dizzy spin of the room. 'It's a bit late for that, isn't it?' she demanded truculently, thinking the dizziness was champagne and she was belatedly being carried over the threshold. 'Where's this?' she demanded, staring past Silas myopically. 'Somewhere sensible, I expect. Sensible shoes, good teeth, always punctual. If you're really wicked you get Paris. Where's the sense in that?'

Silas smiled despite his concern and attempted to place her on the bed. She kept her arms firmly around his neck.

'Rachael. . .' He tried to extricate himself firmly but gently, aware of the muffled giggles from the other side of the bed.

'Why won't you take me to Paris? I'm sick of being sensible and. . .'

Silas kissed her, managing to muffle the flow of words which he had a good idea she'd regret saying in front of him, never mind an audience. It worked. Her body relaxed and her arms slipped from his neck. He watched her settle back into sleep, an indulgent tenderness curving his beautifully cut mouth.

'I'm no Prince Charming.' His tone was light but there was an indefinable tension in the room when he met Amanda Tredegar's gaze.

'She loves you.' Amanda's violet eyes held a mixture of emotions. She had asked too much of Silas and she had never felt it so keenly.

'Rachael understands. There's no threat, Amanda. I'll always be there for you, you know that.'

Rachael murmured, turning her face into the pillow, dark dreams chasing her again. No threat—no threat—no threat. The words echoed over and over again. Then Silas's voice saying 'I love you.' She cried out, the pain too intense, and found herself imprisoned, unable to move. A rocking motion lulled her back into the arms of sleep. Shadows chased her throughout the night, dreams rearing up and tangling with memories, changing them frighteningly then sinking back into the subconscious to be forgotten. She didn't forget the conversation she had overheard, though, and that remained with her when the world righted itself once more.

Rachael eventually felt normal again, three days later, on the Thursday before the scheduled dinner party. She felt weak but the drained, dizzy feeling had gone. Tristan was still in the house. It appeared that Silas had agreed to their staying there for the duration of her illness. Remembering their last fight, that surprised her and she asked for an explanation on his visit that evening.

'Amanda's been looking after Tristan while you've been ill.' Silas sat on the side of the bed, his attitude distant but cordial, a bit like a doctor. 'Scott pleaded with me to let him stay so. . .' He spread his hands, his blue eyes empty of emotion. 'How do you feel?'

'Much better.' She felt hurt by his attitude without being able to pinpoint what he was doing to make her feel like that. 'Have you been sleeping in the caravan?'

'Yes.' He didn't elaborate. 'Presumably Scott is gathering courage for the big announcement. As soon as Tristan is settled here, you're free to do as you wish. Your cheque book and credit cards will continue to be funded. If you decide to get a job, you can depend on me for a reference.' A smile touched his mouth but not his eyes. 'I can give you a list of very ugly employers if you want.'

'I won't make the same mistake twice, Silas.' It sounded like goodbye and she had to fight to make her voice sound normal.

'No, I don't expect you will,' he agreed expressionlessly. 'I'll be back for the dinner party on Saturday; otherwise I'll be in Paris. Amanda's got the number in case of emergencies.' She nodded, not trusting her voice. 'Goodnight, sweetheart.' He kissed her forehead. 'Take care of yourself.'

She watched him go, her face crumpling as soon as he was out of the door. Great harsh sobs shook her body, the sound muffled by the sheet. She had no idea how long she cried for, but the sound of a teacup being placed on the cabinet by the bed made her sniff and peep over the sheet.

Amanda Tredegar viewed her sympathetically, her own face mirroring the sadness Rachael felt, and then she smiled and sat down on the bed.

'Feeling sorry for yourself, or did Silas upset you?'

Rachael dabbed at her eyes with a tissue, aware that she must look an awful sight. 'It's just the virus, I expect.'

Amanda didn't look convinced. 'I sat with you for most of the first night you were here. You were talking in your sleep. Some of it made sense. Oh, don't worry.' She saw the dawning look of horror on Rachael's face, her smile full of self-reproach. 'You didn't tell me anything I didn't know about Tristan. He's Scott's child. I tried to pretend it wasn't true in the beginning but when Mary Deal died Scott was so unhappy. Silas came back and acknowledged the child in a rather businesslike fashion, so I was allowed to bury my head in the sand again. But the truth is impossible to ignore. I began to feel guilty about Silas, the sacrifices he was prepared to make. When I met you, I liked you. I knew I couldn't let two newly married people begin their life together with all the burdens of the past, especially someone else's past.' She picked up Rachael's cup and saucer and passed them to her. 'Poor Rachael.' She chuckled at the sight of her friend's red, puffy eyes. 'Silas is so obviously in love with you that I can't think what you're crying about.'

Rachael hastily drank her tea. Having just been given the sack and assured of good references, she found it hard to believe that Silas even liked her!

'What will you do?' she asked curiously. 'You seem to like Tristan. He's a nice little boy, very lively but. . .'

'You don't have to sell him to me.' Amanda was gentle. 'At first I thought it would be an impossible situation. I toyed with the idea of leaving Scott. I thought he'd find someone else soon enough. But. . .' she winced '. . . I couldn't go, so I decided it was time to tackle the here and now. That's why I came to Winterbrook that day when Silas made the excuse that Tristan had got a cold. I could sense you were an ally, that you were exactly the sort of person I was trying to be. I admired you for taking on Tristan in that practical way of yours. You'd only been in Cornwall for a few weeks and he was so happy with you. That made me ashamed.'

Rachael shook her head in protest. 'The circumstances were hardly the same, Amanda. I can understand how you felt.'

'Scott wasn't totally to blame.' She sighed, looking down a long tunnel into the past. 'The car crash was a fluke—there was a patch of oil on the road. Scott liked to drive fast but he was a safe driver. We both liked fast cars.' She smiled regretfully. 'I suppose we were a little reckless in those days. It's a common enough story. After the crash, I felt ugly, totally undesirable. When they told me I couldn't have children, I dismissed any thought of a physical relationship with Scott from my mind. I couldn't imagine that he would find me attractive and I hated the idea he would be pretending.'

'You must have been very unhappy.' Rachael listened, wide-eyed, her tender heart moved by the story.

'Yes, I suppose I was. At the time, I don't think I thought of it that way. I was rather numb. Scott was tormenting himself about what had happened to me and I was a passive creature, not even reproaching him for the accident. I think it was the total lack of response that made life intolerable for him.'

Rachael could imagine that. Scott was a tempestuous creature. A bare emotional landscape would be a living hell for someone of his nature.

'You asked me what I was going to do. Well, looking after Tristan has been something of a revelation. Funnily enough, I don't see Mary Deal or Scott. I just see a determined, enchanting little rascal who makes me laugh, makes me feel alive and downright tired at times. But it's a nice tiredness. Tristan is Tristan, not an accusation from the past. I want him to live here. I want to rebuild my relationship with Scott and I'd like us to be a family. There, how does that sound?'

'Wonderful,' Rachael applauded, her pleasure genuine. 'I'm so pleased for you.'

A knock at the door disturbed their privacy. Scott came in, looking from one to the other. He had another cup of tea in his hand, which he handed to Amanda.

'I've put Tristan to bed.' He studied Rachael and then angled his head to see her in a better light. 'You're not having a relapse, are you? You look quite flushed.'

'Thank you for the tea, darling.' Amanda gave him a warning look. 'You can go.'

'Girl talk, eh?' He strolled back to the door. 'I don't know what you've done to Silas,' he offered before leaving, 'but I've had more fun talking to a tailor's dummy.'

'Don't take any notice.' Amanda gave him an old-fashioned look and he pulled an apologetic face which made them both laugh and then left the room.

'Well, I've told you my troubles; are you up to discussing yours?' Amanda offered kindly.

'Not at the moment.' Rachael felt her wounds too keenly to air them in public. Besides how could she confide in Amanda?

'He'll be back on Saturday. Whatever it is, he'll have cooled off by then. It can't be too serious. He was so worried about you when you were ill that he stayed with you night and day until your temperature came back down to normal.'

Probably frightened I'd let the cat out of the bag, Rachael thought sourly. He needn't have bothered as it turned out, but she found little pleasure in his meaningless vigil.

She began to think about getting another job. Should she go back to the States or work in Europe for a while? Going home would mean answering a host of unwanted questions. She would never see Winterbrook finished—the thought came unbidden into her mind before she slept. Her dreams were of a bright, newly painted house. She was in the study where the pale peach walls were softly lit by evening sunlight, arched windows showing a glorious view of the moorland, coated in purple heather. And then everything changed and she was outside, watching a strange car pull up in the drive. Tears dampened her pillow. She wanted those people out of her house. . .

CHAPTER NINE

THE day of the dinner party duly arrived. Rachael was rapidly regaining her strength and her fighting spirit returned with it. She was determined not to weep another tear over Silas Tredegar. He could return to his philandering ways and she would do what she should have done three years ago when her feelings first started to get out of hand—run and not look back.

Thornfield House had taken on a new life that had little to do with the dinner party. She presumed that Amanda and Scott had talked, because they had an aura of happiness about them that was infectious.

Amanda beamed at Rachael as she made it down for breakfast rather than have a tray in her room. 'You look better. I hope your appetite has improved; you've hardly eaten enough to keep a bird alive.'

'I think I could manage some toast.' She sat down, peeping surreptitiously at Amanda's glowing countenance, her lashes dropping quickly when the older woman looked up from pouring the tea.

'It's all settled.' Amanda responded to Rachael's unspoken curiosity. 'You've no idea what a relief it's been to get everything out into the open. We both feel the same about that.'

'I am pleased.' Rachael's dark eyes were warm with pleasure. 'We wondered if it would be possible for you and Silas to move in here until Winterbrook was ready, to provide some sort of continuity for Tris. It would be more comfortable than the caravan and we have plenty of room.'

Rachael tried to hide her feelings on the subject. The idea of all four of them in Thornfield truly appalled her. She understood Scott's and Amanda's point of view. Tristan's childhood had been chequered to say the least and if his surrogate parents disappeared overnight it was impossible to judge the psychological harm that might inflict.

'I'll have to speak to Silas.' She ducked out of an immediate answer. 'He might find it difficult to get used to Scott's taking over the role of father. He loves Tris and he wants what's best for him, but. . .'

Amanda looked thoughtful and then nodded. 'Yes, I can understand that. He was a lonely boy, I suppose he identifies strongly with Tristan.' She smiled, winking at Rachael. 'He's got you now—he won't be alone, will he? Do you plan to have a family quite soon?'

Rachael nearly choked on her tea. The irony of it was that although she had visited the doctor and got a prescription for the Pill she had to wait until her cycle started to begin the course. Far from planning to have a family, the total lack of planning of any sort left everything up to Mother Nature. It was something she didn't like to dwell on.

'I don't think we should have a child just to replace Tristan,' she demurred, but happily Scott came into the breakfast-room accompanied by his son and the subject was dropped to be replaced by the demands of the dinner party later that day.

'How's my favourite cousin-in-law?' Scott lifted her hand and kissed it. 'You look almost your old self.'

'Thank you.' She returned his smile, thinking how nice he looked when he wasn't being sarcastic or bitter.

'Has the menu changed again or can I phone in an order to the fruiterers? If you want avocados, we'll have to make sure we order early.'

Amanda handed him a list, smiling fondly at Tristan who went to Rachael and clambered on to her knee.

'Poorly,' he said in crooning tones, clumsily trying to stroke her hair.

Rachael laughed and kissed him. 'I'm better now,' she reassured the little boy. 'Have you been good?'

Tristan nodded solemnly and then mischievously grinned at Scott.

'I've moved everything above his level.' Scott didn't sound too worried. 'He seems to have a million hands. More like an octopus than a child.'

Rachael chuckled. It was nice to see something turning out right. There would be love in this family and a child needed that security to grow into independence. Silas had never had that and she suspected would spend the rest of his life searching for something he was unable to find.

Disliking the thought of watching the clock tick round until the time when Silas would return for the dinner party, she decided she had time to kill before returning to the caravan to choose what she would wear. She looked after Tristan for a while when the large dining-room was being polished and vacuumed and then found herself in charge of the hors-d'oeuvre. The avocados were for the salad which was a wonderful mixture of the avocados mixed with cream cheese, walnuts and olives. Fish whirls provided an alternative, which, she discovered, were rolls of whiting with prawns packed into the centre. There were to be a dozen guests; one or two arty friends of Scott's, the others appearing to be neighbouring landowners.

When it came to early evening, Rachael's work was done. Her dishes were to be served cold. The kitchen was providing delicious wafts of cooking meat. Game pie and roast stuffed pigeons were to provide the main course. There was even a vegetarian lasagne prepared for one of Scott's friends who didn't eat meat. Amanda clearly hadn't lost her touch; everything seemed to be planned well and she left for the caravan with an easy conscience.

She decided to look in on Winterbrook before she

got changed, and waved goodbye to the last of the workmen before entering the house. It was cold inside after the balmy warmth of a summer evening and it smelt of damp plaster. Gingerly, she picked her way past the discarded tools and pieces of unfinished carpentry and went upstairs. The smell of plaster, she discovered, was coming from the newly plastered walls in the upstairs bedrooms. It was beginning to take shape, she realised with a pang of disquiet. She shouldn't have come here; her resolution not to cry was under severe threat.

The caravan was in rather a mess. Newspapers and files intermingled on the small table, a half-empty bottle of whisky fought for a place along with several empty coffee-cups. Silas was usually quite methodical and tidy—she speculated on another hidden aspect of her husband's character. She picked up a carton of milk from the draining board and sniffed it, expecting it to be curdled, but it was quite fresh. She wondered if he was back. It was then she glanced at the newspapers and realised that one was for the day before when Silas was supposed to have been in Paris. Carefully, she let her eyes scan the door and windows. Nothing had been forced.

A sound from the bedroom made her freeze and then the door opened and Silas peered out, the light making him squint. 'Oh, it's you,' he muttered, and turned back.

Rachael was rigid with shock. Silas was unshaven, wearing nothing but a pale blue pair of jockey shorts and looked ravaged by what she suspected was a hangover. He could have caught her virus—she gave him the benefit of the doubt and followed him into the bedroom. The air was stale and smelt of whisky.

'What has happened to you?' she asked, subjecting him to a close inspection. He was back under the sheet, his eyes closed. 'Are you ill?'

'No. But I feel like hell.'

'Self-inflicted, I presume.' She felt unaccountably cross with him. She had seen the charming rogue, been pleasantly surprised by the serious side of his nature, and now she was confronted by the slob.

'Have you forgotten it's Amanda's dinner party this evening? She's gone to an awful lot of trouble and she needs our support.'

'Our support?' His mockery was unsheathed. 'How cosy that sounds. It's not until eight.' He turned away from her, the long length of his back exposed by the movement. 'Wake me at seven.'

Gazing at him impotently, she expelled her breath in an annoyed sigh. 'I thought it would be nice if we arrived early. I think they may make some announcement tonight about Tristan. Amanda——'

'I know. Scott told me,' the muffled reply came from the pillow. 'I'll smile in the correct places, don't worry, darling.'

'Well, if you're going to drown in self-pity——'

'Get out,' he yelled furiously and hurled a pillow at her. She ducked back behind the door.

'Temper, temper,' she goaded, unable to stop herself.

'One more word, Rachael, and you'll find out why Winterbrook got its name.'

Deciding that discretion was the better part of valour, she opted for a shower before re-entering the bedroom to choose her outfit. The mess in the caravan distracted her for half an hour while she tidied it up. Opening the windows, she let in some fresh air. It was going to be a warm evening; the sun was still hot and it was nearly six.

The shower cubicle was compact to say the least, and the spray wasn't that powerful, so it took some time to get the shampoo out of her hair. When she had finished she groped for a towel and realised that she hadn't brought one in with her. With a muttered curse, she banged on the wall.

'Silas.'

He didn't answer.

'Silas!' She thumped harder.

The door opened. 'I can't believe you're drowning.' He surveyed her sourly. 'Towel?'

'Yes, please.' She spoke between gritted teeth.

He virtually dumped the towel on her head and stood back. 'It's the only one; bring it back when you're finished.' He barely allowed her room to pass.

'Yes, well, that's because you left the others strewn around the floor,' she snapped. 'I suppose the laundry is beyond a mega-brain like yours.'

'I leave such things to menials,' he returned acidly. 'The cleaner was sick.'

Realising he was looking for a fight, she smiled thinly. 'And to think I once thought you were charming.'

'We all make mistakes.' He shed his shorts and she slammed the door shut with a disgusted 'tut'.

They were behaving like two children, she reflected as she pursued the exacting task of drawing a comb through her long chestnut hair. She decided to let it dry naturally, liking the ringletted look Cornwall had given her. She supposed he was still blaming her for taking Amanda out of his orbit. Rachael winced as the thought made her brutal with the comb. Finishing the task, she decided to tackle the bedroom while he was out. She began by opening the windows and then stripped the bed, closing the curtains as she discarded the towel and donned the flimsy underwear she was to wear that evening.

She had only brought a few outfits from Winterbrook but she found what she was looking for. If anyone had told her that purple suede could look dynamic she would have laughed and pegged them as an outdated hippy. But seeing was believing. The colour was a deep purple, the jacket bolero-style and the back-split pencil-line skirt stopped at the knee showing a flattering length of leg. She wore a strapless black silk top beneath the jacket and decided on stilettos to match. Gathering her hair into a loose plait, she felt suitably armoured to deal with her contentious husband.

The thud from the shower made her pick up the damp towel. She handed it over and prepared to wait as he took up residence in the bedroom. He was looking better, she noted. When he'd shaved he might look something like human.

'I hope you're going to eat something.' She reluctantly helped him with his bow-tie, aware that he was taking an interest in her appearance for the first time since she had arrived.

'Why? Do I look undernourished? Is this wifely concern?' His temper hadn't sweetened.

'No.' She was insouciant. 'Amanda has spent a long time over the food.'

It was an inauspicious start to the evening. She asked if she should drive. He replied that though life had temporarily lost its charm he wasn't quite ready to meet his maker. Rachael doubted that he would meet anyone so benign and so it went on.

Thornfield provided a temporarily civilising influence. Scott and Amanda welcomed them warmly. Silas went upstairs to say goodnight to Tristan and Rachael was left to exchange small talk with her hosts.

'Is everything ready?' she asked, thinking how nice Amanda looked in a cream two-piece.

'I think so.' Amanda accepted a sherry from her husband and Scott brought Rachael the preferred gin and tonic. 'Fingers crossed.' She looked startled as the first guests announced their arrival by ringing the bell.

The next half-hour was spent in various introductions. Silas returned to Rachael's side, linking his fingers loosely through hers as Michael and Greta joined them. It was the first physical contact they had had for days and Rachael felt a jolt of reaction at the touch of his skin against hers. Silas was drinking mineral water and, seeing her glance, he winced a smile.

'I'm driving,' he explained.

'So you're not staying here tonight?' she enquired, Greta and Michael distracted for a moment as Scott brought them their drinks.

'No.'

'But. . .'

'I have no intention of asking Scott for separate rooms. Smile, darling, people are looking.'

She kept up meaningless social chit-chat until they went into dinner. If Silas was going back to the caravan, she would have to go with him. Scott and Amanda would probably think they wanted privacy after their time apart due to her illness.

The dinner table was a delight. A navy blue linen cloth emphasised the delicate powder-blue design of the dinner service. It was an advertisement for Scott's prowess as a designer and certainly an effective one. Blood-red candles set in ornate silver and a centrepiece of roses in the same shade made a dramatic contrast.

'I call this style,' Greta enthused. She had enhanced the subdued tan suit she had chosen with an overload of gold but carried it well. Rachael smiled fondly at the older woman.

'Don't celebrate yet. I concocted the first course.'

'You did, huh? Well, I hope it's better than what you've been feeding Silas; he's a shadow of his former self.'

Rachael frowned, her gaze sharpening on her husband. She supposed whisky was a rather inadequate diet. Concern managed to filter through the steely barriers she had attempted to construct. All this was hitting him hard—he had lost his old sparkle.

Neither Silas nor Rachael ate much of the elaborate meal although they both made the pretence of participating. The table was an oval shape and although it was customary for the hosts to occupy the opposite ends of the table Scott had taken the seat next to his wife. It reinforced Rachael's premonition that an announcement would be made. After all, Tristan could hardly move out of Winterbrook and into Thornfield without a lot of gossip. Silas and Rachael were seated opposite each other, flanking their hosts, and it was as if Amanda had put them there, the family, sure of their support.

When the table was cleared and the coffee poured, Scott stood up and asked for their attention. Rachael glanced across at Silas to find that he was looking at her. Her eyes skipped back to Scott; for some reason she felt unaccountably hot.

'I've never liked speeches,' Scott began, and gestured to Silas. 'My cousin is the silver-tongued member of the family but I've left too many of my responsibilities to him. One very important responsibility was my son, Tristan.'

The silence around the table showed that his audience were spellbound. It could hardly be news to many of those gathered there but the public announcement had clearly taken them by surprise.

'My wife has agreed to welcome Tristan to Thornfield, and that's something which makes me happier than I deserve to be. I don't deserve these two either.' He gestured at Silas and Rachael.

'Hear! Hear!' Silas interjected, and broke the tension which gripped the table, allowing a ripple of laughter to relieve the atmosphere.

It became easier after that. Rachael predicted it would be the usual seven-day wonder until the gossip became tired and some other tit-bit superseded it. The only thing she worried about was whether Tristan's grandparents had been consulted about the change in circumstances. When she asked Silas, he nodded and said he'd talked to them the day before.

'Scott's right.' She forgot his earlier fall from grace. 'You have done an awful lot for him. . .and Amanda,' she added, admiration shining in her eyes. 'You can be a very nice person at times, Silas.'

A brief smile curled his mouth. The party had moved back to the lounge, which had been cleared for dancing. They stood near the french windows, which were open, bringing in cooling air from the gardens.

'You can be a very nice person *but. . .*' he interpreted her sentence and its underlying proviso.

Gazing up at him, she was captivated by the warmth of his regard. Less than four hours ago, he had been scrapping with her; now he was turning up the heat in a way that made her unbearably confused. The only conclusion she could come to was that he was making the best of a bad deal and wasn't averse to having company in bed that night.

'You're inconsistent.' It was half an answer to his question, half an accusation.

'I'm boringly consistent, my love. You're just too blinkered to see it.'

A prickle of awareness made her shiver and his keen blue gaze noted the effect he had on her, his smile unacceptably smug.

'Stop looking at me like that,' she reprimanded him, glancing around the room, rather surprised to find they weren't the centre of interest.

'You look stunning in that outfit.' His voice would have charmed the birds off the trees. 'Not quite as brazen as the black denim battle-dress.' A wicked gleam came into his eyes. 'You've certainly matured since you've been with me.' His hand slipped inside her jacket to warm her ribs. Watching the hectic storm of emotions play across her face, his eyes darkened. 'Let's get out of here. I want to talk.'

'But it's early,' she protested, but glancing at the clock she was surprised to see it was nearly eleven.

'No, it isn't. And besides, you've been ill.' He caught her fingers with his and drew her along behind him.

Scott walked to the door with them, his eyes bright with subdued amusement. 'Will we see you in the morning?' he enquired with a tactful lack of innuendo.

'I'll be back for breakfast,' Rachael assured him, thinking of Tristan.

'Don't count on it.' Silas caught his cousin's wink and exchanged a purely male look of understanding, which, had Rachael intercepted it, would have made her reflect darkly on 'male chauvinist pigs'.

The caravan was a much more welcoming sight than it had been that afternoon. Watching Silas secure the door, she wondered if they were about to ring the bell and come out fighting. In the month or so they had been married, she had gone through nearly every emotion in the book. Her relationship with Geoffrey had been kids' stuff. It certainly hadn't prepared her for a man like Silas.

Turning to face her, Silas subjected her to a searching appraisal. 'Me first,' he suggested ungrammatically.

She shrugged, her expression wary. 'You said the bit about my credit cards and references. What else is there to say?'

His lips clamped together and then he frowned. 'That's one of your options. You know I want you to stay.' His lean, dark countenance became harsh and demanding. 'I'm not an international playboy living a glitzy carefree existence. I get hurt just like anyone else. I prefer an old house on a moor to fume-choked cities; if that disappoints you, I'm sorry. But look on the bright side.' He came closer, his voice dropping. 'I turn you on just looking at you, and that's not something you find every day.'

She realised she'd slapped him when the crack and the sting of her hand confirmed the action. Eyes blazing, her chestnut hair confirming a powerful temper, she launched into the attack.

'Are you trying to suggest that I wanted that kind of life? You have an extraordinary talent for self-deceit.'

'Really.' He rubbed his jaw, the menace in his eyes telling her not to try the same trick twice. 'You keep on telling me how distinctly lacking in glamour my life is. You seem in a big hurry to leave now that Tristan's finally settled. What am I supposed to think?' Pushing his fingers through his dark hair, he gave her a burning look. 'You're the only woman I'll ever ask to be my wife. The only woman I want to have my children. I need you, Rachael! Don't you understand?'

She did. Silas's world had turned upside-down. He didn't want to lose everything at once. She knew the feeling!

'I don't want to hurt you, Silas.' All the pain she felt showed in her eyes. 'I know you care about me, but it's not enough.' She put up a hand when he went to interrupt, fighting down a feeling of panic when she realised it was time for the truth. Walking to the far window of the caravan, she took a deep breath, closing her eyes for a moment before she turned to face him.

'I know how much you care about Amanda. I suppose I feel the same way about you. It's a living hell to want someone you can't have but I can't live with that for the rest of my life. It hurts too much!'

Silas froze, staring at her with an odd expression in his eyes. 'Amanda,' he repeated slowly, as if talking to an idiot.

'Yes. Don't pretend. Scott told me you'd been in love with her when you were young. Everything was for her, wasn't it? Our marriage, this whole pretence, even the final resolution was for Amanda.'

'Scott,' he repeated, looking extremely aggravated. 'I'll swing for that cousin of mine.'

'I don't think he knows you still feel that way——'

'Damn right,' Silas grated, eyeing her with a malevolent expression. 'And he's not going to, because it's not true. The work of a fevered imagination, if you ask me.'

She refused to give ground, her stance defiant and proud. 'Fevered I might have been, but my hearing wasn't impaired. Amanda told you that I loved you and you reassured her. You told her your feelings wouldn't change, that she could always depend on you. You told her you loved her!' Her voice pressed home the point like a prosecuting attorney but a tear ran down her cheek in a totally enchanting contrast.

'Rachael.' He approached her, shaking his head, his expression softening, the warm glow in his eyes back and confusing her even more. 'You—er—care that way about me.' He recalled the other part of her admission. 'What did you say? It's a living hell wanting someone you can't have?'

'Yes.' She backed off until her calves came into contact with the bench at the back of the caravan. Slapping away his hands, she refused to be side-tracked.

'OK.' He made a calming gesture, aware of the shine of tears in her eyes and finding it frustrating trying to comfort her from a distance. 'I did reassure Amanda. I suppose she was at a crossroads in her life. She was on the verge of deciding to challenge Scott with the truth and there I was, her strongest ally, totally wrapped up in my flu-ridden wife.' He closed in on her, watching the defensive flicker of her lashes. 'I didn't tell her I loved her. That was later, when you were upset. I couldn't calm you. I was scared your temperature was going to go through the roof.' His eyes pleaded with her to believe him. 'I love Amanda like a sister. But she's not the woman I want. She hasn't got your strength, your fire. She's not you! Rachael—if I can't be near you or hear your voice, I'm in the wilderness. Those two weeks you were in Iowa nearly killed me. . .'

Rachael wanted to believe him but didn't trust Silas when he started to lay on the blarney. 'So why did you get drunk?' she accused him, prodding a finger at his chest. 'I thought you were upset because Scott and Amanda were getting back together at last. Was it Tristan?'

'Partly,' he admitted, watching his finger make a pattern along the shoulder of her jacket. Blue eyes flicked back to hers, the intensity of his expression startling her. 'I liked coming home to you and Tris. I found I preferred it to empty hotel rooms and restaurant meals and women who cared more about my ability to pay the bill than the company they were in.' Fingering a strand of her hair, he regarded her with a smoky sensuality that nearly made her forget everything, including her own name. 'When you were ill, you seemed upset that I'd never taken you to Paris. We did go to Paris once, didn't we? I'm sure you went with me on the Cordeau deal.'

Rachael went red. 'Yes, we did. I was delirious, I was probably thinking of somewhere else.'

He didn't look convinced but let the subject drop. 'I have a confession to make, Rachael.' He tried to take her in his arms but she resisted, a warning in her eyes that made him respect her wishes. 'I. . .you've been important to me for a number of years.' Looking distinctly uncomfortable, he made his confession. 'You were so young and naïve when you first came to work for me that I had to force myself to leave you alone.' He watched the disbelief grow in her eyes. 'Greta used

to make very acerbic remarks that kept me in place.'
He slid his hands around her waist. 'Don't push me
away, darling,' he murmured against her ear, pulling
her close. 'I did try to do the decent thing but when
Geoffrey started pawing you in public it made me see
red.'

Rachael felt stunned. 'Why didn't you tell me?' she
asked, avoiding his marauding mouth as he tried to kiss
her.

'I thought you were besotted with Silas-the-Cad.' He
spoke against her lips. 'I wanted you to know the real
me, love me as I am; the problem was, I wanted to get
you to bed so desperately that I don't think you noticed
the difference.'

'I do love you,' she whispered, closing her eyes as
Silas crushed her lips beneath his in a long, hard kiss.
Her heart lifted, happiness singing along her veins,
hard-chased by another more compulsive emotion. Her
mouth clung to his, her fingers plucking his shirt out
from the wasitband of his trousers and sliding with
ardent possessiveness over the line of his spine and the
smooth brown planes of his back. Silas moulded her
against him, stroking the suede that fitted snugly over
her buttocks before loosening the zip. Urging it from
her thighs, he caressed her silken skin, before turning
his attention to her jacket.

'I'm going to love you all night,' he promised, his
tone ragged. Burying his face into her throat, he
groaned as she succeeded in getting rid of his jacket
and shirt. His skin was hot to touch and she could feel
the tremor in his body as well as the hard, masculine
demand.

'When I found out Michael had those gambling
debts, it felt like Christmas.' He talked but his gaze
roved over her near-naked body. He watched her
release herself from the black silk top, his hands
smoothing her wayward mane of hair back into place.

The black lacy teddy she wore underneath made him give a mock growl of appreciation. 'I hadn't a clue how to approach you,' he admitted, his eyes narrowing on the provocative pout of her mouth. 'Are you listening to me?'

Framing his face with her slender hands, Rachael kissed the base of his chin. 'Do you really love me?'

'I think I must.' His eyes crinkled into a smile at her sheer delight. She wrapped herself around him and he picked her up, laughing at the shower of kisses that covered his face and throat. 'It's time you were in bed,' he murmured in an intimate tone as she placed baby kisses around his mouth.

'I suppose I shouldn't over-exert myself,' she agreed, remembering the virus and knowing he hadn't meant that at all.

Placing her on the bed, Silas paused to remove his trousers, aware of her lazy appraisal. The only light came from outside the door in the living area; neither of them wanted the harsh electric glare the bedroom light provided.

Rachael felt as if a great weight had been lifted off her shoulders. She no longer had to hide her delight in his masculine perfection. He had a wonderful physique, broad-shouldered, with tight, well-toned musculature. Pulling the black briefs he wore down over his hips, he joined her, his warmth drawing her to him, her eyes flickering over him and meeting his in a blatant sexual enticement.

'You're powerful stuff, Red.' He bent his head to the soft, pink seduction of her mouth. Their lips brushed and then clung, her teeth parting as she welcomed the intrusion of his tongue.

There was nothing leisurely about their lovemaking. It was hot and hard and left no room for anything but the soothing of aching senses.

She had promised herself that she would live in a

tent with Silas and follow him to the ends of the earth if he really loved her. A crack of thunder rolling across the sky and the loud patter of rain on the metal roof reminded her of that promise. She didn't regret it. If Silas preferred a house on a moor and caravan holidays then so be it. She would follow her man anywhere. And he was her man! She gripped his shoulders, pressing her face into his neck as he gathered her to him. The lightning sang along her veins, electrifying every vulnerable nerve as she moved with him to a shattering crescendo of passion that branded her his forever.

CHAPTER TEN

RACHAEL held the door open for one of the men who were moving the furniture back into Winterbrook. Some of the more durable items had been upholstered and restored. Standing, hands on hips, she scrutinised the study. It was still her favourite room in the house and with the alterations to the windows it now gave view to the promised vista of purple moorland. The dark wood panelling had been replaced by a mock-panelling effect painted in the soft peach shade, brightening the room immeasurably. An American sofa of black-painted bamboo and coral cotton upholstery, matched with two straw-coloured canvas chairs, enhanced the ambience of softness and light. A large desk stood in a window recess set on the Bessarabian rug, the flowered pattern on a blue background tamed by the base carpet, a deceptively tough plain weave pattern. A smile of satisfaction curved Rachael's mouth. It was just how she'd pictured it.

'Daydreaming again.' Scott dusted his hands off on his jeans and took in the newly painted room. 'Not bad for two philistines. Trust Silas to disappear when there's hard work to be done. I suppose he's living it up somewhere exotic.'

'Lyon.' She sounded as wistful as she felt.

Michael entered, carrying a tray of coffee-cups, followed by Kitty, who enthused over the kitchen. Far from being nostalgic about the old Winterbrook, the ever-practical Kitty maintained that it should have been done years ago. 'It was that old skinflint George Tredegar—he wouldn't spend a penny on a lick of paint.' She sat down on the new couch, accepting a cup of coffee from Michael.

'I hope Silas likes it.' Rachael knew that her husband was the most likely candidate to mourn the old house. 'He was very fond of it the way it was.'

Scott grunted sceptically and Michael, who liked comfort, looked mystified. Her brother had moved to London and had a flat in Chelsea. He was enjoying a rather raucous social life but hadn't as yet shown signs of gambling again. Rachael knew that Silas had a network of contacts who would report on any defaults in that direction and Michael was in awe of his brother-in-law, accrediting him with what amounted to omniscience when it came to his misdemeanours.

Amanda and Tristan arrived when the furniture had been placed to Rachael's satisfaction. Scott produced two bottles of champagne and they toasted the new Winterbrook. Showing Amanda the upstairs rooms, they both marvelled at the fresh, airy effect that had been created. The guest bedrooms were individual in their design. They entered the rose room. The walls were sponge-painted in pale pink and white, the newness of the plaster making wallpaper unsuitable. The bed was covered in an exquisite ivory-white lace cover, chintz curtains with a small rose design and in-built wardrobes with louvered doors completing the effect. 'Oh, isn't this lovely?' Amanda's violet eyes lit up. 'We'll have this one when we stay.'

Rachael grinned. 'Scott said it would be like being engulfed by an ice-cream, so you might have to negotiate.'

Tristan thudded down the hallway and launched himself at the bed, squealing with delight as he bounced back up again.

'Tristan, get off there at once!' Amanda gave Rachael an apologetic smile and secured the wriggling form, explaining that everything was new and he mustn't break anything.

Rachael watched them together with a warm feeling. The honeymoon period was over; Amanda was as apologetic as any mother with a boisterous infant bent on creating chaos in someone else's house.

Michael was the last to leave. He surveyed her critically. 'Do you want to come to a party? It would be better than sitting here feeling sorry for yourself because Silas isn't here.'

'No, thank you. I've got a lot to do. And I do not feel sorry for myself. I just miss him.' She swallowed a lump in her throat. 'Thanks for asking.'

'I can stay if you like,' he offered grudgingly, reddening as she chuckled.

'Thank you again, but I won't keep you from the bright lights.'

It was quiet when everyone had left. She tidied away the empty bottles of champagne and the soiled glasses. It had been nice having Michael and her new family helping her to move in but she couldn't help resenting the fact that Silas wasn't at Winterbrook to see the house finally finished.

They had spent most of July living between Thornfield and the caravan. It had been a pleasure to watch the bonds between Scott, Amanda and Tristan grow. Silas had relaxed considerably over the matter. She had been concerned at first, wondering how he would adapt. Silas had brought the subject out into the open one night after they had left Thornfield and had been viewing the progress on their own house.

'You seem tense when we're staying with Scott and Amanda. Is anything wrong?'

'No.' She was a little too quick to reply and he had caught her arm, bringing her to a halt; surveying her discomfort with a frown.

'Scott hasn't——?'

'No!' she had denied the irrational male jealousy,
casting him a chiding glance. 'It's nothing like that.
I. . .well, I thought it might be hard for you. . .with
Tristan. Is it?' she'd asked, hoping he could pick up
the sense from her garbled explanation.

'I suppose I always knew he'd go back to Scott. . . It
seems right for him to be at Thornfield.' He had linked
his arms around her waist, his gaze watchful. 'Do I
seem uncomfortable with the idea?'

'No.' She'd fiddled with a button on his shirt. 'It was
just that you blamed me for changing things.' She'd
revealed the source of her past anxiety. 'It was like
being asked to join some secret society. You'd all
shared childhood experiences. I felt like imported stock
of   inferior   quality,   brought   in   to   maintain
appearances.'

Silas had shaken his head, his mouth curving indul-
gently. 'I've always valued your unclouded vision. I
used to envy the old-world morality you projected. It
was time for things to change but I'd invested so much
in maintaining the pretence. You were part of that.'
Eyes as blue as the Cornish sea beguiled her. 'I wasn't
going to use Michael against you if you left me. All I
had to hold you was Tristan. I loved you both and. . .it
was the first time I've had a family like that. It was
hard to lose. . .'

As if on cue the phone rang and, such thoughts
forgotten, she smiled with pleasure as she recognised
her husband's voice.

'Rachael?' He was brief. 'I need some figures bringing over tonight. Greta will give you the details. Mac
will drive you to the airport——'

'You want me to bring them?' she clarified, surprised. 'I mean—when? I'll need to pack.'

'Don't worry about that. You can buy anything you
need. Just find your passport and get ready.'

Rachael was busy checking the house was secured

when Greta arrived. She had packed an overnight bag and located her passport but that was all.

The older woman handed over the briefcase. 'Like old times, huh?' she joked. 'Did he tell you to bring your pad and pencil.'

'No.' She reflected on the unadorned instructions. He had hardly been very lover-like, not even wasting time to say hello.

'Silas didn't say much at all. He seemed in a hurry.'

'Oh.' Greta smiled mysteriously. 'Well, this should do the trick.' She patted the briefcase. 'I'll see you when you get back. I've met this real nice guy, a widower with his own decorating business.' She widened her eyes expressively and Rachael chuckled.

'Where am I supposed to be going—Lyon?'

'Hard to say. He's on the move. Don't worry, Mac will have an update on the latest situation. Here he is now.' She nodded towards the window as the BMW cruised into sight.

Mac had little more to offer. 'I think you're flying into Paris. There should be somebody waiting for you at the airport.' And so it went on.

She arrived at Charles de Gaulle airport just as it was getting dark and was sped through the suburbs of Paris into the city itself. Deposited outside the Challoner Hotel, used by Tredegar and Pitt's top executives when in the French capital, she entered the exclusive environs, to be greeted by the desk clerk.

'Ah, Miss James.' The clerk no doubt thought the journey was responsible for her bemused expression. 'Mr Tredegar said you'd be arriving tonight.' He handed her a key. 'He left a message to say he'll call later.'

'Thank you.' Accepting the key he handed to her, she thought no more of the clerk's assumption that she was still Silas's secretary until she got to her room. And room it was! Not unpleasant but merely a bed, a wardrobe and an armchair. On the bed was a jeweller's box and in the window alcove a huge display of red roses. Putting down her holdall and the briefcase, she gave rein to her curiosity and went over to pick up the jewellery box and opened it. Inside was a diamond pendant with matching earrings. A card fluttered to the floor and she stooped to retrieve it. On it was a room number and the message, 'Dress for dinner; you'll find what you need in the wardrobe. S.'

Totally bewildered, she opened the wardrobe door to find an indecent creation in jade silk, a pair of strappy sandals and on a separate hanger the sort of delicate lingerie that could only be bought in Paris.

'I don't understand any of this,' she muttered, glancing at the red roses with a feeling of disquiet. Silas knew how she felt about them. Why had he chosen that particular flower? Picking up the hanger, with the expensive underwear in the same jade colour as the dress, she went through to the shower. And why such a small room? Was there a business function at the room he had specified? Then it became clear. Of course, Silas must have booked a suite elsewhere. He had arranged for the room so that she had somewhere to bathe and change. The roses she allowed as an oversight.

Viewing herself thirty minutes later, she fastened the earrings and considered the finished result. Long auburn hair curled over her shoulders, the diamond pendant resting just above the line of her cleavage. The jade complemented the golden-tinted tone of her skin, deepening the colour of her eyes, making her look like—like some rich man's mistress! Her hand went up to yank the pendant from her throat but she didn't complete the gesture. Turning, she looked over her shoulder into the mirror. The dress left her back uncovered, showing the smooth, unblemished skin. Whatever Silas's motives were, she suddenly felt swamped by a restless, burning need to see him. The shimmering silk of the dress luxuriated against her skin. It was so light that she felt almost naked.

Taking the lift, she discovered that the function was in the penthouse suite. The lift opened out into a small, plushly carpeted reception area and a uniformed hotel security man allowed her to pass.

'Rachael,' Silas greeted her, tall and impeccably attired in a dark evening suit. The all-encompassing glance he gave her made her shiver pleasurably but the intimacy of his gaze lacked something.

Casting him a perplexed glance, she walked past him into the opulence of the suite that appeared to be otherwise empty.

'I have a distinct feeling of *déjà vu*.' She remembered the other occasion when she had expected to act as a hostess for Silas and had received his bizarre proposal of marriage. A tap at the door heralded the arrival of a trolley laden with silver dishes.

'When were you last in Paris having a candlelit dinner with your boss?' Silas queried silkily.

'Silas! What is going on?' She watched him tip the waiter and close the door. 'Is this your suite? Why did you book the room for me two floors below?'

'I thought you'd prefer it. For appearances' sake,' he added, approaching her with two glasses of champagne, handing her one and smiling down at her. 'Married men have to be discreet when they plan liaisons in Paris.'

'But we're——'

'Shush.' He placed a finger over her lips. 'It's a warm night; we'll have dinner outside, shall we?'

The roof garden was beautifully scented and provided an exquisitely romantic setting. Below them, the sound of Paris could be heard, the occasional horn of a car, friends calling out to each other, the eternal hum of traffic.

'Oh.' Rachael sat up straight in her chair. 'I've forgotten the briefcase. . .' Suddenly she saw the light. It all came together. Paris, the roses, the gift, the separate room. Her eyes were bright when they met her husband's. 'How did you know?' she asked with a husky chuckle.

'I'm telepathic.' He accepted her on to his knee, shaking his head in mock reproach. 'Wicked women don't get enthusiastic, they flirt and tease——'

Rachael fulfilled an overwhelming need to kiss him. Silas accepted her fall from grace, his mouth hardening against hers as she relaxed into his embrace, her mane of hair spreading over his arm.

'I suppose I must have told you when I had flu.' She closed her eyes as he nibbled at her ear.

'Mmm, you said you were sick of being sensible.' He brushed his lips over the curve of her cheek. His fingers stroked over her shoulders, watching her as she eased back and began to undo his bow-tie. 'The food here's very good. Aren't you hungry?'

Those blue eyes were lethal, Rachael acknowledged without an ounce of regret.

'It would be a shame to waste it,' she agreed, trying to keep her mouth straight.

'Not very sensible at all.' Silas continued what she had started, unbuttoning his shirt. 'I thought we'd have a belated honeymoon.'

'You're not working, then?'

'No.' Silas's eyes narrowed as she stroked the muscular wall of his chest. 'There's this sexy redhead driving me to distraction.' His eyes closed and he swallowed as she began to kiss the hair-roughened skin. 'I'll show you the rest of the apartment,' he offered thickly, picking her up in his arms and pushing himself to his feet.

'Just the bedroom,' she requested provocatively,

nuzzling behind his ear. 'Silas, would a wicked woman ever say "I love you"?'

'Frequently.' He urged the bedroom door open with his shoulder. His eyes ran over her hotly. 'Without a great deal of sincerity. The trick is sounding as if you mean it.'

'Oh.' She considered this, catching his wrist as he placed her on the coverlet and urged him down beside her. 'I think I must be doomed to being sensible, then.'

Silas's laughter was low and intimate as he surveyed the tousled picture she made, the jade dress riding up around her hips, one shapely knee rubbing against the dark material covering his thigh. 'Darling. . .' He bent to brush her lips with his, growling his pleasure as her hands worked their erotic magic. 'Believe me, you're wicked enough.'

Next month's Romances

Each month, you can choose from a world of variety in romance with Mills & Boon. These are the new titles to look out for next month.

NO GENTLE SEDUCTION Helen Bianchin

THE FINAL TOUCH Betty Neels

TWIN TORMENT Sally Wentworth

JUNGLE ENCHANTMENT Patricia Wilson

DANCE FOR A STRANGER Susanne McCarthy

THE DARK SIDE OF DESIRE Michelle Reid

WITH STRINGS ATTACHED Vanessa Grant

BARRIER TO LOVE Rosemary Hammond

FAR FROM OVER Valerie Parv

HIJACKED HONEYMOON Eleanor Rees

DREAMS ARE FOR LIVING Natalie Fox

PLAYING BY THE RULES Kathryn Ross

ONCE A CHEAT Jane Donnelly

HEART IN FLAMES Sally Cook

KINGFISHER MORNING Charlotte Lamb

STARSIGN

STING IN THE TAIL Annabel Murray

Available from Boots, Martins, John Menzies, W.H. Smith, Woolworths and other paperback stockists.

Also available from Mills and Boon Reader Service, P.O. Box 236, Thornton Road, Croydon, Surrey CR9 3RU.